Mrs Barron.

Nelly - anne

26 th oct 93.

0426832233
813130

DAVID PEAT

In Search of
Nikola Tesla

ASHGROVE PRESS, BATH

Published in Great Britain by
ASHGROVE PRESS LIMITED
7 Locksbrook Road Estate
Bath, Avon BA1 3DZ

ISBN 1 85398 020 X

First Published 1983
New Edition 1993

for
Maureen Doolan

Photoset in 11/13 Plantin by
Ann Buchan (Typesetters)
Walton on Thames, Surrey
Printed and bound by Redwood Books,
Trowbridge, Wiltshire

Contents

Page

PREFACE   7

Chapter One   9
Chapter Two   12
Chapter Three   23
Chapter Four   34
Chapter Five   48
Chapter Six   53
Chapter Seven   58
Chapter Eight   66
Chapter Nine   74
Chapter Ten   84
Chapter Eleven   92
Chapter Twelve   100
Chapter Thirteen   107
Chapter Fourteen   115
Chapter Fifteen   123
Chapter Sixteen   127
Chapter Seventeen   133

POSTSCRIPT   142

Preface

NIKOLA TESLA WAS either one of the most creative minds the world has ever known – or he was a blatant fraud.

The alternatives seem extreme and dramatic, yet as I look through the patents and articles which cover my desk I am forced into this polarization. For Tesla was no ivory tower scientist who published cautious reports and qualified extrapolations from the security of some academic haven; rather he was a bold and original thinker who claimed that the discoveries he had made would lead to social revolution.

On July 3, 1899, Nikola Tesla claimed to have tapped an 'inexhaustible source of power' which could be beamed across the globe. In the future which Tesla foresaw, the world would be linked by a net of endless energy, need would be abolished, the deserts would flower, arctic wastes would become fertile, cities of the future would be clean and free from disease, war would be abolished and humankind would turn its eye outward to the civilization of the stars.

These predictions sound like something from the pages of Jules Verne or his English counterpart H. G. Wells. But Tesla was an engineer and businessman who had already harnessed the power of Niagara Falls and taken the first steps in the construction of an electrical power network which would one day stretch across continents.

Nikola Tesla was no impractical dreamer and his claim to have discovered an inexhaustible source of power was repeated over and over again in articles, personal letters and public letters. There is no element of doubt in these statements, no qualification, no element of caution until further experiments are performed.

Tesla was emphatic. The man who had outstripped Thomas Edison in inventive power claimed an even greater victory, the ability to direct power without loss anywhere on the planet.

If the claim is correct and has simply been ignored by conventional science then society has been robbed of an enormous crock of gold which sits at the end of the electrical rainbow. Or could Tesla's pronouncements and predictions have been based on a fiction? Had the brilliant young inventor turned into a peddler of fraudulent dreams?

The answers to these questions take us into curious and unexplored territory, for until a few years ago Tesla's plan for worldwide broadcast power had been forgotten, buried beneath a stack of patents and articles which date from the turn of the century. I, as a scientist, had barely heard of Tesla's name and knew virtually nothing about his life.

One day, however, a curious set of circumstances forced me to reach into that mass of yellowing patents and examine a claim which had all the appearance of science fiction. I was asked to test the feasibility of Nikola Tesla's vision of the future. In doing so I came across something even more surprising, the claim that Tesla's devices had already been built in Russia. If this was true then the dream had turned into a nightmare, for there were rumours that this technology was being used to change the world's weather and exert some curious form of mind control over sections of the earth's population.

The stories I unearthed seemed even more fantastic than anything Tesla could have dreamed up but I had been offered a challenge and I had accepted. Now I was to reach back from my position in the twentieth century and touch the mind of a genius whose greatest invention had been made almost a hundred years earlier. In many ways this task was to become the culmination of my own scientific ventures. I felt that I was ideally suited to meet such an adversary as Nikola Tesla.

Chapter One

Dr Schneider, President of Canada's National Research Council, reached forward and took a folder from his desk. He opened it and read in silence the letter at the top of the file. Then, without looking up, he asked me: 'What do you know about Nikola Tesla?'

I floundered for a moment at the unexpectedness of the question. I had been surprised that morning to receive a request to visit Dr Schneider in his office, having recently resumed my work as a theoretical physicist at the Council after a year's sabbatical in London. Clutching at the only straw I could find I hazarded: 'The Tesla Coil. I suppose Nikola Tesla must have invented the Tesla Coil'.

I think that in my position any other scientist would have answered in a similar way. Anyone who has spent time in a research laboratory which contains a vacuum system of pumps, globes, meters and glass tubes will have used a Tesla coil. It looks something like a screw driver with a heavily insulated handle and a blunt metal tip at the other end. Leading from the handle is a length of electrical flex which is plugged into the nearest socket. Once plugged in, the instrument begins to vibrate and hum, for it is a pocket sized gadget for generating high voltages and high frequencies.

A Tesla coil is used to detect leaks in vacuum apparatus. If the vacuum inside a glass tube is 'good' then a blue glow will be seen inside when the tip of the coil is placed next to the glass. With undergraduate students the coil has another use, for it can be placed close to the trouser seat of a colleague as he bends to retrieve a fallen object from under his bench. The results of this operation are quite dramatic.

The utilitarian and comic aspects of the Tesla coil and the assumption that someone named Tesla must have invented it were all that I could muster in response to Schneider's question. He must have been following my thoughts for he smiled.

'Tesla did far more than that; in fact he was responsible for the world's first electrical power project. He harnessed the energy of Niagara Falls and took it to the city of Buffalo.'

I was surprised at this information: why had his name not seemed more familiar to me?

'I thought that Edison or Westinghouse developed electric power,' I said.

Schneider continued: 'And there are claims that he did far more than that; the extraction of gases, a remote controlled boat, even radio communication.'

'Oh come on,' I interjected, 'I won't go that far. We all know that Marconi invented radio.'

Schneider paused and looked down at the file. 'There is a group of people who think that Tesla did some pretty dramatic things. It's all documented here but I really don't have time enough to deal with it properly.' He smiled at me. 'I was hoping that you would look at it for me.'

I was puzzled. If Tesla had worked on the Niagara Falls power project then he must have been active at the turn of the century. He must have died decades ago. Why was the Research Council interested in a set of inventions which could be anything from fifty to a hundred years old?

'What these people are saying,' Schneider continued, 'is that Tesla's biggest discovery has been ignored by the scientific world.'

'You mean he's some sort of forgotten genius? What is it that he's supposed to have invented?' I asked.

'Oh, something very surprising: Broadcast Power! He claimed that he could send electrical energy anywhere across the world without the need for wires and what's more, without any losses at all. One hundred per cent efficient.'

'But that's crazy. Broadcast power like that won't work. What on earth did he mean?'

Schneider turned over several pages of the file. 'Some of our own people have had a look at his invention and they don't think much of it. But we have to go in to it more carefully and give these people a proper answer. It's not going to be all that easy.'

He handed me the file and I began to turn the pages casually. An item from a newspaper caught my eye. I turned the clipping over and read it quickly. It was about radio interference of the short wave band, Russian experiments, high voltages. I noticed that Tesla's name was mentioned several times. I remembered that the Tesla coil would produce interference and smiled to myself.

'I don't suppose the idea is to build a giant Tesla coil, is it?' I joked.

Schneider did not smile back: he continued to look at me, then said. 'Possibly. It may be something like that.'

I began to protest but Schneider stood up, the interview was at an end.

'Take the file with you and see what you can make of it. Talk to anyone you need and then write me a report.'

I turned to walk to the door and heard his voice again. 'And let me have that report within a month or two. There's some political interest in all this, it's not the sort of thing that's going to go away.'

Chapter Two

BACK IN MY office I opened the file, unclipped the documents and arranged them on my desk. As I sorted through the papers I began to experience a feeling of excitement and anticipation. It was a recollection of something which must have happened in the past. I realized that it was the smell and feel of these papers which had brought memory flooding back. I was a young man, sitting in a University library with a typed manuscript on my knees. This was my first day of scientific research and a few hours ago I had faced my professor. He had simply handed me the manuscript and said: 'This is a thesis of one of my students; take it away and read it. It's quite an interesting problem so think about it and see what you can come up with.'

I left his office with the papers in my hand and no clue as to what I should do next. The interview had produced no explanations, no suggestions or directions: I was simply to be left to my own devices. That afternoon as I sat in the library with the thesis before me I was filled with fears and doubts but at the same time a curious exhilaration – what if I was unable to understand the thesis? What if I could not think of a new approach? Was my career in science to end that very day? I realized that I was now on my own, that in one sense I had become linked to the scientific community and, like the great scientists in the past, I too was faced with a problem whose mysteries I would fight alone.

All my life I had been fascinated by science.

Born in Liverpool a few months before the outbreak of the Second World War, my earliest memories are of explosions of lights in the sky over Liverpool and journeys in the middle of the night across our tiny garden to the air raid shelter. But there is a stronger memory. It is of visits to my Aunt and Uncle's house away from the bombing; visits which included books full of exciting pictures, of stars and planets, volcanoes and microbes. I can remember that even before I could read I would sit beside my Aunt hour after hour and ask her to talk about these pictures.

As I grew a little older I began to build a laboratory in the coal shed outside my home and, until darkness drove me indoors, I would experiment with gases and acids and all the transformations of matter which were at my disposal. At school the subjects of chemistry and physics offered little magic compared with the wonders I could create in my secret laboratory, yet one teacher in particular began to open a new world to me. He showed me how the myriad facts and wonders of nature, all observations and phenomena could be linked together through reason and logic to form a scientific theory. He also hinted that the theory itself possessed its own unique beauty.

A seed had been planted. In my late teens, I went to pubs and tennis club dances, attended University and argued all night on any topic under the sun. But my thirst for knowledge continued and I spent the long winter evenings hunched over an electric fire trying to keep warm with a textbook on my knee.

A few years later I had obtained my first degree and had begun scientific research. There was a challenge in all this yet, at the same time, the romance had been tarnished. It seemed that, for those around me, research involved small problems and narrow fields of enquiry. As I was worrying about the direction my experimental research should take I met another creative teacher. He was a theoretical physicist and showed me that the world of the imagination need have no bounds, that through mathematics it was possible to create a scientific universe which is limited only by one's ability. In theoretical physics I would be able to plunge through a problem at the speed of thought, I would feel the very shapes of ideas and speculations. It was not many weeks after my first discussion with this man that I renounced the chemist's laboratory forever and turned to theoretical speculations.

Scientific papers were published; a few years passed. I came to Canada, taught at a University, then moved to the Government research institute in Ottawa. For a time I was content, absorbed in the various physics problems before me. I had music and books in the evenings, friends who would drop in for a chat. I visited conferences in Europe and the States, gave lectures and wrote papers. But as I gained confidence in my abilities I began to take a closer look at the direction I was taking. I wondered how my research and that of my colleagues would look in a historical perspective. From many other scientists I gained the impression that the great days of discovery were over. That in most cases, they would say, we knew the rules which made nature tick. If it was fundamental problems that I was after then I had arrived on the scene fifty years too late.

In the first decades of this century physics had been in a turbulent state. The first tentative probes at the Quantum Theory and Einstein's Theory of Relativity had shaken its foundation. Out of that confusion had grown a new science of greater beauty and power, a physics which reached deeply into the heart of nature. For many who worked in the second half of this century it seemed sufficient to do homage to the New Science, to evaluate its implications. The highest ambition would be to dot an 'i' or correct the punctuation in the book of nature but never to dream of re-writing it. For those interested in experiments there were still speculative fields like astronomy and biology but for the theoretician, modern Quantum Theory was here to stay. It had been better tested than any other theory in the history of knowledge and scientists were stuck with it for decades or even centuries into the future.

Yet I had not entered science simply to wander along well trodden paths and clean up in the wake of giants who had gone before me. For the excitement as a boy had lain in unexplored worlds and in theories which made me giddy by their audacity. I began therefore to study the foundations of modern physics and after some hard thinking came to the conclusion that the modern attitude of acceptance of Quantum Theory was far from appropriate. I saw that there were difficulties deep within the heart of physics, that the new science had been built on two incompatible theories, two behemoths who were in a state of eternal and sluggish war. Einstein's theory of Relativity and the Quantum Theory had been created almost at the same historical period yet they were based on very different views of the world and on different intuitions as to the way nature works. It was t' e general feeling amongst scientists that the differences between the two theories could be resolved through ingenious mathematical manipulations, rather as if a cold war between two superpowers could be denied simply by printing new maps of the world. I began to realize that this incompatibility between two approaches to nature could be terribly important, that it could be an indication of the new directions science must take to bring it into a deeper understanding of nature. In some ways I felt the situation was not unlike that which faced Einstein at the turn of the century when he considered the incompatibility of Newton's Theory of Mechanics and Maxwell's Theory of Electro-magnetism.

Preoccupied with these ideas I took a sabbatical in London and spent most of my time with two scientists, David Bohm and Roger Penrose. They were both concerned with these problems but had different creative approaches. My year spent in London was free and stimulating. I spent evenings at the theatre or in pubs near the college talking for hours about these scientific problems. In an eclectic way these talks ranged far beyond science into linguistics, psychology, mysticism and perception, and through them I began to realize that the way to a new science did not lie simply in developing new mathematics or setting up new experiments but would arise from a radically new way of looking at the world. Science of the twenty-first century had to learn a different way of asking questions of nature.

The investigation of nature is never a passive process in which facts and theories fall half formed into a scientist's lap and wait to be fitted together. Gathering data isn't like picking up attractive shells on the beach. It is an 'intentional' process in which the phenomena uncovered are, to some extent, a reflection of the way each question is posed.

An example may help. Suppose that an international group of physicists build a bigger and better elementary particle accelerator. What secrets of nature will they uncover?

In a sense they are asking nature a 'leading question'. For their enquiry is based upon a number of presuppositions – for example that, at its most fundamental, nature is composed of particles, that we can investigate matter by bombarding it with high energy 'projectiles', that at higher energies newer and more interesting elementary particles will appear. Now all of these presuppositions may be quite correct, or they may be only partly correct. What is clear, however, is that they are not the only suppositions we can make about the ultimate structure of matter.

When it comes to the investigation of nature scientists always run the danger of becoming convergent in their approach. Questions asked within the context of a particular theory tend to confirm and reinforce that theory. They may be irritating and badly behaved facts that never quite seem to fit but these can always be patched together by additional assumptions.

It is only when the whole process has reached schizophrenic proportions that some scientific revolutionary comes on the scene and shouts, 'Stop. What's nature *really* trying to tell us?'

This had happened in the first years of the century when Einstein had overthrown Newton's Mechanics and founded his new Theory of Relativity. Likewise Heisenberg, Schrodinger and others were able to follow the clues given to them by Planck, Einstein and Bohr in formulating the Quantum Theory.

During my sabbatical in London I had come to the conclusion that we were facing such a crisis yet again in modern physics. While so many scientists were attempting to patch together Relativity and the Quantum Theory and resolve such internal inconsistencies as the infinite self-energy of the Vacuum State, I felt that a totally new set of questions must be asked.

I was reminded of P. G. Wodehouse's creation, Jeeves. When the perfect butler was faced with an obnoxious quest or his master's formidable aunt, together with a plethora of lost telegrams, newts in the bathtub and purloined policemen's helmets, he did not rush about looking for the way out of the problem. Instead Jeeves would contemplate what he called 'The Psychology of the Individual'. Armed with an understanding of the way his master's antagonist would think and act Jeeves could then rise above the problem. It was not so much a matter of 'solving' anything, more that the difficulties just dissolved in the white heat of the butler's fish-fed brain. With all that nonsense out of the way Jeeves could get on with the real problems of the world such as the choice of a tie or the exact shade and cut of a jacket.

I felt that scientists should take a leaf from Jeeves's notebook by learning the 'Psychology' of modern physics. Instead of trying to patch-up their stricken theories they should realize that incompatibilities in theoretical structure were pointing us in new and surprising directions.

It was with such stirring revolutionary thoughts in my head that I returned to the National Research Council after my year in England.

I came down to earth, to Nikola Tesla. I was back in the present with a new problem in front of me. But had things really changed that much? I might have published a score or more papers and lectured before various scientific organizations, but in the end each new problem was a challenge and I was just as naked before this new challenge as I had been in that University library many years before.

I went back to the papers on my desk and tried to make order out of them. I soon realized that the story would be difficult to piece together since the file itself was not the work of one author. In place of the usual proposal with summary, index, introduction, exposition, references and technical appendix were a series of letters, minutes of meetings, photocopies of old lectures, documents and patents and what looked like a scientific paper.

The main proposal came from an international group based

in Canada called P.A.C.E. or the Planetary Association for Clean Energy which had devoted itself to the study of Nikola Tesla's patents and writings. For his part Tesla was represented by some letters, copies of speeches, patents and drawings, most of which dated from the turn of the century.

As I looked through this material I was puzzled as to why Tesla's name had escaped me, and why the Tesla coil was his only invention which had come to mind. I went over to my bookshelves and took down a standard textbook on electricity. Sure enough, the index contained the names Edison, Westinghouse, Farady, Ampere and a host of other scientists, but there was no entry corresponding to the name of Nikola Tesla.

I went back to my desk and began to look through one of the documents written by the Planetary Association for Clean Energy. It contained predictions of the important consequences of Broadcast Power. It spoke of modifying the earth's weather, cleaning polluted atmospheres and repairing the ozone layer. The paper went on to describe plans for transporting fogs, disintegrating icebergs, mining the sea bed, producing pure water from the oceans and fixing fertilizers from the air. The picture painted by these proposals was of an earth made fertile by the abundant power which could be broadcast across the globe.

This future vision of the world had the flavour of a short story by H. G. Wells. It was predicated upon the virtues of a scientific discovery and on the way a golden age could grow out of technological innovation. In contrast with the development of atomic power and microbiological research in our own age, these future powers would be used only for the public good; there would be no horrific side-effects or catastrophic conclusions which society would have to pay on demand.

This thinking seemed to me almost as dated as the illustrations which used to accompany Mr Wells's visions of the future. P.A.C.E. appeared to have escaped the pessimism which so many others had developed for science through the last decades. It ignored the horrors of modern war, the unthinking application of new processes, Thalidomide disfigurement, disruptions of delicate control system by insecticides and the pollution of lakes and rivers.

There had once been a time when the world had had faith in a technological future but now it had become cynical and disillusioned by the promise of new breakthroughs and advances. It seemed to me that the Planetary Association for Clean Energy possessed a faith in science which was distinctly unfashionable. But, as I gathered their papers together, it struck me that while their approach had seemed obver-enthusiastic, the basic premise was not too bad. P.A.C.E. was concerned with the earth's supply of energy and with the distribution of this energy across the globe. This was a very sensible notion and one which scientists had been urging as far back as I could remember. Even at high school, I had read that our natural energy resources would soon be at an end, that energy would become concentrated in the hands of a minority and a sudden shortage would be disastrous. While some nodding acknowledgment had been given to these ideas, it had taken an increase in the cost of heating homes and running a car before an energy crisis could be taken seriously. Now it had happened and people were beginning to panic, newspapers carried wild suggestions by a variety of experts and private groups talked of burning wood and erecting solar panels on their homes. P.A.C.E. seemed to have recognised the seriousness of the problem and that it must be solved in a rational way on an international level. Even if the theory of Broadcast Power should prove to be wrong, at least their approach seemed reasonable.

I decided to go home early. I had become fascinated by the project and wanted a little time to myself, free from the telephone and good natured interruptions. I walked out of the building and across the snow to the bus stop.

An hour later I was at home and hard at work, the Tesla documents in my hand. I began with the story of the Russian radio interference. According to the newspaper report it had been bad enough to disrupt short wave communications at repeated intervals. Protests had been sent to the Russian Government by a number of European countries. But did this interference have anything to do with Tesla transmission? It seemed clear that something along the lines of an enormous

Tesla Coil would interfere with radio reception but was a Tesla Coil the only possibility? I could think of other experimental electrical devices which might have similar effects. There did not seem to be much point in speculating and I decided to call a couple of colleagues next morning who might be able to help me track down some hard facts about radio interference.

I began to read through a lecture Tesla had given in 1927. As I absorbed his words I began to see what had fired the members of P.A.C.E. Tesla seemed to radiate an immense confidence in the significance of his discoveries. There was no trace of that caution and qualification which was found in the average scientific lecture. Tesla was bold and determined when he wrote:

> The transmission of power without wires is not a theory or a mere possibility, as it appears to most people, but a fact demonstrated to me in experiments which have extended for years. Nor did the idea present itself to me all of a sudden but was the result of a very slow and gradual development and a logical consequence of my investigations which were earnestly undertaken in 1893 when I gave the world the first outline of my system of broadcasting wireless energy for all purposes. In several demonstrative lectures before scientific societies during the preceding three years, I showed that it was not necessary to use two wires in transmitting electrical energy, but that one only might be employed equally well. My experiments with currents of high frequencies were the first ever performed in public and elicited the keenest interest on account of the possibilities they opened up and striking character of the phenomena. Few of the experts familiar with the up-to-date appliances will appreciate the difficulty of my task with the elementary devices I had then at my command, as accurate adjustments for resonance had to be made in every experiment.
>
> The transmission of energy through a single conductor

without return having been found practicable, it occurred
to me that possibly even that one wire might be dispensed
with and the earth used to convey the energy from the
transmitter to the receiver.

I read on and found that Tesla had required special currents
for his experiments. First he had designed new dynamos, then,
concerned by their limitations, he had turned to novel devices
to produce high voltages. I realized at this point that he was
referring to something that sounded very much like a Tesla
Coil. He spoke of this coil in connection with his experiments
on radioactivity which he boasted were 'prior to the discovery
of Radium' by the Curies. With the invention of this coil he
felt that he had given the scientific world a 'veritable lamp of
Aladdin.' These were certainly not modest or self-effacing
words, indeed he sounded like a proud parent speaking of a
talented child. Yet, for Tesla, this was only the beginning.

As I think of my earliest coils, which were nothing more
than scientific toys, the subsequent development seems
like a dream.

I had the sensation that I was drawing close to the heart of
Tesla's discovery when I read of an experiment he had
performed in 1899 at Colorado Springs. The result was
staggering, for he claimed that, at the turn of the century,
electrical energy was sent across the entire globe to return with
undiminished strength.

It was a result so unbelievable that the revelation at first
almost stunned me. I saw in a flash that by a properly
organized apparatus at sending and receiving stations,
power virtually in unlimited amounts could be conveyed
through the earth at any distance, limited only by the
physical dimensions of the globe, with an efficiency as
high as ninety-nine and one-half per cent.

This was the kernel of Tesla's plan for world wide energy

transmission. Its origin was an experiment performed at the end of the nineteenth century. Could it actually have happened? Had Tesla stumbled upon a hidden quirk of nature, a phenomenon of electro-magnetism which had since gone unnoticed?

It seemed incredibly far fetched that such an experiment should have been neglected for the next eighty years. With so many laboratories and scientific installations across the world, with the millions of dollars invested in the electrical industry, surely someone would have taken an interest in Tesla's results and repeated his experiment or, through very weight of scientific research, have come across the same phenomenon simply by accident. But despite these doubts I could not deny that I was attracted by the audacity of Tesla's claim and I was forced to ask myself, 'What if it were true? What if it had actually happened?'

I returned to the manuscript and read to the end of Tesla's lecture. Now I felt he was stretching credibility too far, as he described the manner in which the electrical power was broadcast from his transmitter. Although the text was not always clear he seemed to be saying that the waves of energy left the tower at infinite speed then slowed down until they were travelling at the speed of light. Once they had crossed the equator they speeded up again until they reached the Antipodes at an infinite velocity. Later on he said that this was only an apparent effect for in fact the waves did not travel *around* the earth. They penetrated deep through the core to reach the receiver by a path directly through the earth.

As I put down the pages I realized I was totally confused. Somewhere there must be some more comprehensive explanation of his power transmission, possibly in one of the patents. I made a mental note to track down all his Letters Patent.

It seemed almost too much to take at one sitting. I began to think how we take so much scientific fact 'on trust'. Most of what we know comes out of books and published papers which we assume are basically honest. To reach the pages of a scientific journal each paper must pass through a referee system and we have a tendency to accept this process as being successful. It is true that occasionally genuine errors are published. Once they appear in print there is a danger that they will perpetuate themselves from publication to publication. Yet, in the end, an incompatibility between several scientific observations or a contradiction between theory and experiment leads a careful researcher to retrace the steps back to the error which found its way into the original paper.

But small slips and occasional errors are a different matter from deliberate deception. If a scientist were to carry out a conscious plan to change or even invent experimental results, would the resulting fraud be that easy to expose? After all if a research worker makes the claim that a series of measurements have been made or a particular phenomenon observed, few scientists would demand to visit the laboratory and see the hard evidence with their own eyes. Much is taken on trust.

If a hoax were to be carefully planned and executed, then the forged results would be internally consistent and would easily fit into an existing theory. Once formulated this fraudulent data could well prove a false trail for a great many scientists.

I recalled that there had been precedents - the Piltdown Skull had been an assumed genuine by many experts. Arthur Koestler had written about a hoax in biology in *The Case of the Midwife Toad*, although he felt that the alleged fabrication had been unjustly condemned.

In the seventies it had even been discovered that false results had been reported by the eminent psychologist Sir Cyril Burt. Burt had been the prime mover behind the modern trend for psychological testing and was particularly interested in the relative significance of environmental upbringing and genetic make-up in such factors as I.Q.

Some of Burt's most significant work had involved sets of identical twins who had been split up by adoption at an early age. Since their genetic make-up could be assumed to be identical, any differences in their abilities should be the result of different home environment. Burt drew conclusions from his observations which influenced a whole generation of psychologists and filtered down to new teaching methods in schools. Imagine the horror when, after Burt's death, it was discovered that many of these identical twins had simply never existed. In order to present effective statistical data for his hypothesis, Burt seems to have invented some of his subjects and fabricated their raw data.

Here was a clear case of a scientific fraud which had deceived hundreds of research workers and had been perpetuated in countless learned publications. No wonder the idea of a scientific hoax is as repellent to the scientific community as sexual deviation would have been to the Victorian middle-class. Just as lesbanism had never been added to England's criminal code due to Queen Victoria's famous refusal to believe such an act possible, so it seemed that many scientists would be almost prepared to accept the impossible rather than believe a colleague guilty of deliberate deception.

I began to realize how complex my reactions were to Tesla's lecture. Here was a scientist who claimed to have observed a phenomenon of such importance that to accuse him of having made a casual mistake, a slip of the tongue or a careless observation was out of the question. My initial reaction was that either Tesla was mad, a liar or, and this seemed equally absurd, that he was correct.

I began to wonder what sort of a man Tesla had been. Apart from the papers provided by P.A.C.E., I had very little evidence of his actual existence. Not one of my textbooks made mention of his name beyond referring to the Tesla Coil. Was he indeed a scientist of repute and the inventor responsible for modern power transmission as P.A.C.E. claimed?

I went across to my bookcase and began to search through the *Encyclopaedia Britannica*. Sure enough, in Volume 18, there was an entry for Tesla, Nikola; born in Smiljai, Croatia, in June, 1856. What first caught my eye on that page was not the text, but a photograph: Tesla as a young man, handsome, dark and with penetrating eyes. He had been placed in a formal, almost Victorian pose by the photographer. His cheek rests on his left hand and his face is turned towards the camera. Well greased black hair is parted symmetrically into two waves and he has a small neat moustache. There is a curve to his mouth and the lower part of his face looks thin and sensitive, but with a certain tension as if any expression was to be kept tightly under control. Around the eyes, something of humour seems to dart, but it is the eyes themselves which give the photograph its whole quality. The line of the shoulder, of the left wrist, the movement of the lapel, even the slope of the ornamentaton of his chair bring us back to the eyes. For a moment I could almost swear that the photograph had been touched up, that a skilful photographer had manipulated something of the depth of the eyes in order to give the image more power.

The encyclopaedia article gave the bare facts of Tesla's career. He had trained as an engineer at the Universities of Graz and Prague and then worked for the Edison company in Paris. His experiments with electrical machines were described and, in 1884, emigration in poverty to the United States. A year later, Tesla had sold the patent rights of his electrical inventions to George Westinghouse. Westinghouse was later to use the machines in the Niagara Falls Power Project which provided the city of Buffalo with electricity in 1896.

Tesla appears to have spent the money he obtained from his inventions in building a laboratory. There he experimented with x-rays, electrical lighting and alternating currents. A few years later, financed by J. P. Morgan, America's most powerful banker, he constructed a second laboratory in Long Island, New York, from which he attempted to perfect world-wide radio broadcasting. This latter project seemed to have failed, not so much through scientific obstacles, but out of severe financial difficulties. From that time, Tesla became increasingly reclusive and eccentric. He was given to proffering pronouncements to the newspapers concerning communications with other worlds, death rays and secret weapons. He died in 1943 and his notebooks and writings found their way back to his native Yugoslavia.

Beyond his achievements, what picture of Tesla the man emerged from this article? The only hints as to his personality were references to a dreamer with a poetic touch, and 'self-discipline and a desire for precision,' which seemed rather vague generalizations. There was an enigmatic sentence towards the end of the article:

Though he admired intellectual and beautiful women, he had no time to become involved.

What lay behind that statement, I wondered? At the end of the encyclopaedia article was a reference to a biography which I determined to follow up in the library the next day. There was much to be done in the days which followed: I would get hold of all Tesla's patents; track down those stories about radio interference; and there was something which I had to find out as soon as I got into my office next day – to my embarrassment I could not remember how a Tesla Coil worked.

Chapter Three

THE TESLA COIL is a device which is so commonplace to the scientist that I had always taken it for granted. As I looked through the advanced textbooks on electricity and magnetism I was unable to find a circuit diagram for the coil but when I turned to a more elementary compendium of physics I found what I had been looking for.

As I sat at my desk, looking at the circuit diagram, I had the insight that the key to the Tesla Coil is Resonance. The importance of resonance had again cropped up in the papers I had looked at the previous evening.

This idea of resonance, I was to discover, lies at the heart of many of Tesla's inventions and is the key to his experiments on Broadcast Power. Resonance is not so much a law of nature as a manner in which nature works. In a sense Resonance is one of nature's habits, for it extends right across science from electricity to steam engines, from molecular dynamics to the tone of a musical instrument and from the rattle of a railway carriage to the tuning of a radio.

All sytems in nature have their own particular way of vibrating: for example the swing of the pendulum in a grandfather clock, the notes on a violin, waves on a lake, vibrations of a tuning fork, oscillations of an electric circuit, signals from a Pulsar. Resonance describes the way in which large quantities of energy can be exchanged between such systems when their vibrations coincide.

As a simple example, think of a little boy on a swing who has not yet learned to 'pump' his legs. His father sends him kicking and screaming high into the air with one hefty push. The child swings back and forth, then shouts for more as his father pushes him again. Now suppose that father gets bored and wanders off to look at the ducks. The pushing is left to his young daughter who just doesn't have the same amount of muscle power. What can she do?

Being a smart child, the daughter uses the idea of resonance to send her little brother high into the air. By giving a series of small pushes, timed to coincide exactly with the natural oscillation of the swing, she is able to transfer energy from her arms into the swing. If the timing is not right, then the swing behaves in an erratic way, but if the pushes are 'in resonance', then each impulse adds progressively. The child goes higher and higher through the cumulative effects of a series of small pushes; in this way a large amount of energy can be transferred from the arms to the swing.

In the same way, an opera singer will pitch her voice exactly to the natural vibrational frequency of a glass. By holding the note 'in resonance' with the glass, energy is transferred. This transferred energy builds up to a point where the molecular structure of the glass is under such a stress that it disrupts and the glass shatters.

Other examples of resonance are not hard to find: the sudden increase in clarity of a radio station as it is 'tuned in' or, in scientific terms, as the resonant frequency of the circuit in the receiver is brought into resonance with the broadcast signal.

Soldiers who march across a suspension bridge, in step, are in danger of exciting one of the modes of vibration of the bridge if their rate of marching is in resonance with the swing of the bridge, so that the bridge begins to swing from side to side with increasing violence.

Nikola Tesla had used this same 'habit of nature' in his invention of the coil which has been named after him. Making use of resonance in several stages of the device, he discovered a way of generating very high voltages and frequencies using ordinary household electric current and a device small enough to fit into the hand.

A Tesla coil consists of three main circuits: A, B and C. Conventional energy, from a normal electric circuit, is brought in at A and the novel phenomenon of high frequency and high voltage discharge occurs at the spark in C.

Conventional power, fed into A, finds itself on one side of a transformer. This transformer has the effect of 'stepping up' the voltage from A into the second circuit B.

The higher voltage in C would be free to go around in a complete circuit but for a break in the circuit called a 'spark gap' G_1. If a spark occurs at G_1, then some current flows through the circuit for an instant but, in the intervals between sparks, no current flows. The overall effect is a current which is in a stop-go condition. As the sparks fly faster and faster this current vibrates rapidly between an Off-On situation. In effect B contains a current of high voltage and high frequency – but still not as high a voltage as Tesla requires.

The crucial piece of the device is the third circuit C. It may not look very different from B, again the current could go round in a complete circuit but for the spark gap G_2. The two circuits B and C are connected through a transformer which produces even higher voltages in C. Probably the most important feature of the third circuit C is its variable condenser which has the effect of 'tuning' the circuit. This variable condenser acts in the same way as the variable condenser in a radio set is used to select a station. By changing its capacity, it becomes possible to change the natural frequency of electrical vibrations in the third circuit. The secret of a Tesla coil is to vary the condenser until its natural frequencies, of B and C, come into resonance. When this resonance occurs, it is possible to pump energy into C.

This ingenious device makes it possible to take normal household current and convert it into very high voltage and high frequency current. The spark gap G_2 in the Tesla coil can be made a fraction of an inch long of many feet across as the dimensions of the Tesla coil are altered. An engineer can build a Tesla coil to any dimension he wishes so that it can be used for anything from the production of artificial lighting to the testing of the vacuum in a small laboratory system.

As I made notes on the coil I began to wonder how the same ideas of resonance had been worked into Tesla's theory of power transmission. That was something which I would have to puzzle over during the next weeks.

After ordering from the library the Tesla biography I had noticed the previous day I decided that my next job would be to track down the facts behind those stories of radio interference. It did not take me many telephone calls to find a reliable source of scientific information.

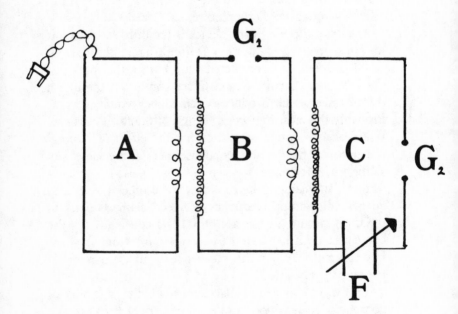

RADIO INTERFERENCE

The frequencies used by international short-wave broadcasting stations lie between 4.5 MegaHertz (four and a half million cycles per second) and 30 MHz. Most stations are grouped into 'bands' of frequencies between these two limits. In terms of wavelengths, these are the 11, 13, 16, 19, 25, 31, 41, 49, and 60 metre bands.

Radio hams, marine radios and aircraft make use of lower frequencies in the 1.6 to 4.4 MHz range and even lower frequencies are used for conventional AM broadcasts.

The peculiar interference signals, monitored in April of 1977, for example, were observed at around 6, 7, 8, 9, 10, 11, 12, 18, 20, 21 MHz which places them well within the International Shortwave spectrum. The interference itself consisted of regularly repeated bursts of pulses of electrical energy and had considerable strength.

During the April, 1977, monitoring period the pulse rate was at 9.615 Hz and at other periods, burst of pulses occurred 5 to 15 times per second. These frequencies are all within the range of the natural resonant frequency of the earth itself – the Schumann Resonance.

Triangulation of the signals indicated that their origin was somewhere in the neighbourhood of Riga in Russia's north west.

Beginning early in 1976, heavy interference had been recorded in Europe and North America. The disturbance occurred in the short wave band, between 3 and 30

MegaHertz – the range used by international broadcasting. In some cases, the effects were so intense that international communications on certain frequencies were 'blacked out' for several hours. It was not long before monitoring agencies had taken a 'fix' on the source and pinned it down to a location just outside Riga in Latvia.

Protests were made from London, Washington, Ottawa and other capitals and, towards the end of 1976, the Russian government admitted that they were conducting experiments which could give rise to radio interference. The exact nature of these experiments was never revealed but the protests themselves seemed to have had some effect for the interference was cut down to a series of short bursts over limited time intervals.

The considerable range of the interference suggested a generator of very high radio power – possibly operating at over five million watts. There seemed little doubt that the Russians had built a device which produced a great deal of electrical power. Could it be a Tesla Transmitter?

The high frequencies of the interference seemed odd. I checked back into the Tesla file and confirmed that the Tesla resonance was at low frequency, only a few cycles each second, instead of the millions of cycles per second observed by the monitoring stations. However, when the interference patterns were closely analysed, they were found to occur in pulses repeated at regular intervals – machine gun bursts of power. The frequency of these pulses lay between 5 and 15 times a second – the Tesla frequency!

Clearly, secret electrical experiments were taking place in Russia. But were there other possible explanations before a Tesla transmitter was invoked?

I remembered once listening to some conversations on communication during a nuclear war. If it ever came to pass that a large number of hydrogen bombs were detonated, then conventional radio communications would become impossible because of extensive interference and ionization from the nuclear explosions. The problem then was for a country to maintain contact with its missile-carrying nuclear submarines deep under the ocean. How could this be done? One suggestion was to make use of radio waves at very low frequency – just a few cycles per second. This radiation is fairly impervious to interference and would penetrate under the sea to submerged submarines. Now low frequencies mean long wavelengths. A United States proposal called 'Project Sanguine' had come up with the design for an antenna a million metres long which would be looped for convenience over an area of a billion square metres.

Possibly a Russian version of 'Project Sanguine' already existed and was sending out test transmissions. However, unless some curious new modulation effects were being investigated, the signals would be in the low frequency range and nowhere near the millions of cycles per second which were being picked up by angry short wave listeners.

Another possibility which occurred to me was 'over the horizon radar' which I knew was being investigated in several countries. Conventional radar is used to plot the path of inocming aircraft or hostile missiles but is limited in range since the beam cannot 'bend' over the horizon. If the target is too far away then it is effectively 'over the horizon' and as invisible to conventional radar as it would be to a man with a telescope. One solution is to extend the 'line of sight' of the radar by placing the set in an aeroplane and flying as high as possible. The higher the radar set then the further away it can spot an intruder.

An alternative approach to airborne radar is to 'bounce' the signals over the horizon. The experimental testing of such an 'over the horizon radar' station seemed another plausible explanation for the Russian signals and one which the experts in radio communication seemed willing to accept.

By the end of the morning I felt that I had accomplished a great deal. I now knew that the newspaper stories of radio interference were based on fact although it was not yet clear what sort of experiments were responsible for the signals.

That afternoon I began to read through the documents on my desk. I tried to find out a little more about the Planetary Association and what kind of people were trying to revive Tesla's plans for world-wide power transmission. As I looked through the list of names I noticed that few of them were associated with a University or research institution. It seemed that P.A.C.E. was composed of what could be called 'concerned individuals' rather than experts in science or engineering. Several of the addresses were Canadian and one of the names was that of a Canadian senator, but what struck me immediately were the name of Andrij Puharich and Marcel Vogel.

Vogel's name rang a distant bell; I recalled that he had been involved in experiments on thought transference in plants. In the mid-sixties a man named Cleve Backster had been investigating polygraphs or 'lie detectors'. For amusement he connected one of the electrodes to the leaf of a plant in his laboratory and watched what happened when he watered the pot.

One of the ways a lie detector works is to measure the resistance of the subject's skin, for even the smallest increase in sweating produces a drop in electrical resistance – water is a good conductor of electricty. As any student of electronics would have expected, the same thing happened when Backster watered his plant – the polygraph showed a deflection. But as Backster continued his experiments, he came to believe that plants experienced some primitive form of 'feeling' and response just as animals do. When a plant was damaged, it seemed to feel pain. When other plants or animals in the room were harmed, the plant connected to the polygraph responded. Backster began to wonder if all life, from human down to the simplest vegetable, was part of a web of intercommunication.

Marcel Vogel had read of the Backster experiments and tried to go one step further. He claimed that by putting himself or a volunteer into a relaxed state, it was possible to project thoughts and feelings to house plants. By connecting a leaf of the plant to a polygraph, it was then possible to make an objective record of its response. Vogel went further. He began to project bursts of 'mental energy' over long distances to the plants. In one experiment he claimed to be able to affect a plant in California from as far away as Prague, Czechoslovakia.

I noticed that Vogel's address was given as San Jose, so I put through a call to a friend of mine who had worked at the big I.B.M. installation in that city. Half an hour later he phoned back; yes, he knew a little about Marcel Vogel, who appeared to be a mixture of research chemist and free-wheeling inventor. He had published a number of scientific papers in the field of liquid crystals, and had been responsible for the coating used on the memory discs of modern computers. The latter invention had been worth a great deal to I.B.M. so Vogel could now do more or less as he wished. As I put down the phone I realized that Vogel sounded a little like Tesla himself – an inspired inventor with far-from-orthodox interests.

In the case of Andrija Puharich, I did not need to make any phone calls, his name was well known to me. Puharich was an old hand when it came to fringes of science. After obtaining his M.D., from Northwestern University in 1947, he had begun a lifetime research into the paranormal with side excursions into the field of medical electronics.

During my visit to Birkbeck College, there had been considerable interest in the Israeli psychic, Uri Geller, who had given a number of demonstrations displaying his ability to bend keys, read minds and even move metal objects by a form of thought control. Laboratory results on Geller's power were ambiguous and difficult to interpret. They had not been made any easier by the publicity given to him by Puharich.

This American researcher into parapsychology must be given the credit of first 'discovering' Geller and urging scientists in the United States and Britain to subject the Israeli's abilities to scientific scrutiny. But things didn't stop there, for Puharich hypnotized Geller and then questioned him about the origin of his powers. The results of these sessions were published in a book written by Puharich, which told of flying saucers and beings from other planets who controlled Geller's psychic energy.

A scientist interested in the paranormal was one thing but the paranormal *and* flying saucers seemed the limit. I had once asked Uri Geller about the claims made in Puharich's book. He laughed and said that such things shouldn't be taken too seriously. I wondered if perhaps Geller had invented the stories, even on an unconscious level, in order to please Puharich.

If Geller's alleged abilities were astounding then even more so were those of Puharich's first prodigy, Jose Pedro de Freitas, nicknamed 'Arigo' or the 'Surgeon with the Rusty Knife'. Arigo was born in Congonhas do Campo, Brazil, in 1918. As a young man he worked as a labourer, a farmer and later in a small café. At about the age of thirty be began to suffer periods of depression and sleeplessness which were attributed to spirit possession.

Arigo travelled to the state capital, Belo Horizale, where he stayed in a small hotel. One night he rose from his bed and walked into the room of another guest. What is supposed to have happened next is scarcely credible. Arigo is said to have told the occupant to lie down, then, taking out a small penknife, he plunged it into the man's chest and removed a piece of tissue.

According to the Arigo legend, the man, named Bittencourt, had recently been diagnosed as having a maglignant tumour in the lung. After Arigo's nocturnal attack the tumour is supposed to have vanished.

The healer's legend spread, and more and more sufferers flocked to his 'waiting-cum-operating room' in his native village. By 1963 Puharich had flown down to experience Arigo's medicine first-hand and later returned with a team of doctors and medical technicians.

The study group confirmed one thousand instant diagnoses, often made by Arigo in the correct technical jargon after looking at the patient for a matter of seconds. According to Arigo he himself took no conscious part in the process but was guided by the spirit of 'Dr' Adolphus Fritz.

For some diseases Arigo prescribed drugs, for others it was kitchen table surgery. I had once seen a film of Arigo operating. The 'surgeon' did not bother with any of the modern techniques of antiseptics, sterilization, anaesthetics, blood clamps or even sutures. Picking up the nearest knife and wip-ing it on his sleeve, he appeared to plunge it into the body and complete the operation within seconds. The wound itself was said to heal without infection or discomfort to the patient.

To our sophisticated minds, such cures and diagnoses seem totally absurd and we are inclined to dismiss the 'Surgeon with the Rusty Knife' as a charlatan. But what of Puharich's medical team, would they have been deceived in hundreds upon hundreds of cases? Either Arigo's powers were real or it appeared that Puharich himself was party to a gigantic deception.

After this first study, Puharich had flown back to the States to obtain additional equipment, but before he could return Arigo was dead. I had been told that Puharich had been deeply distressed by Arigo's death, for he felt that the key to a medical revolution had slipped through his grasp.

With the Brazilian healer dead, Puharich had lost his chance to make detailed recordings and analyses of what he felt to be 'medical miracles'. After Arigo's death he had moved to a study of Geller and now, it appeared, to an attempt to resurrect Nikola Tesla.

The picture I began to piece together was of an obviously clever man who was concerned with the 'leading edge of science'. Puharich had obviously pursued this field of myth, legend, elusive fact and half truth with incredible energy. As I looked through the P.A.C.E. proposal, I realized that a theoretical explanation of Tesla's energy transmission had been written by Puharich himself. What sort of theory would a man of such diverse interests and talents compose? It seemed to me that P.A.C.E. had more than its fair share of brilliant eccentrics.

Chapter Four

OVER THE NEXT few days I managed to obtain photocopies of several of Tesla's patents. Whether or not Broadcast Power worked he had certainly been prolific.

One of Tesla's earliest patents, No. 382,279 dated May 1, 1888, was for an electro-magnetic motor and began in high style:

> To all whom it may concern:
> Be it known that I, Nikola Tesla, a subject of the Emperor of Austria, from Smiljan, Lika, border country of Austria-Hungary, now residing at New York in the country and State of New York, have invented certain new and useful improvements in Electro-Magnetic Motors, of which the following is a specification ...

This was in all probability one of the patents Tesla had sold to George Westinghouse and the inventor certainly seemed proud of his achievement:

> These motors present numerous advantages, chief amongst which are their simplicity, reliability, economy in construction and maintenance, and their ease and dangerless management. As no commutators are required on either the generators or the motors, the system is capable of very perfect action and involves but little loss.

Tesla was right, previous motors had used a system of 'brushes' or mechanical connections between fixed and rotating parts of the device to carry the current. At high speeds this connection would crackle and spark so that the motor operated in a highly inefficient way.

Patent after patent dealt with new electrical machines, systems of power transmissions and improvements to earlier inventions. Towards the bottom of the pile was a heavy folder which dealt with such inventions as 'a novel method of and apparatus for producing light by means of electricity'. That sounded interesting. I pulled out the Patent and began to read. What Tesla had done was to pump out almost all the gas from a glass globe. By applying high frequency current at high voltage, the sort of thing he could produce with his coil, he found that the gas inside would glow. Tesla mentioned that for light to be produced there did not even need to be a completed circuit between the bright globe and the electrical generator. Today we would understand that a high frequency *field* had been induced in the globe, but I imagine that such a phenomenon must have mystified Tesla's friends in the nineteenth century.

I opened another file and my eye was caught by a patent for an 'Apparatus for the Utilization of Radiant Energy'. This one was dated November 5, 1901 and Tesla now described himself as 'a citizen of the United States, residing at the borough of Manhattan'. I recalled from my undergraduate physics that during the last decade of the nineteenth century there had been considerable interest in the mysterious radiation produced in cathode tubes. It had variously been called cathodic and Roentegen radiation. Scientists had asked themselves if this phenomenon was a new type of radiation or, on the other hand, a beam of tiny particles. According to the Patent, Tesla decided on the latter.

> My own experiments and observations, however, lead me to conclusions more in accord with the theory heretofore advanced by me that sources of such radiant energy throw off with great velocity minute particles of matter which are strongly electrified ...

Tesla then went on to suggest that these beams of charged

particles could be used to control electrical machines by acting as an ultra high speed switch.

Clearly Tesla was not only a scientist at the forefront of knowledge but an inventor, seeing practical advantages in each new discovery, no matter how exotic it might be.

In addition to a box piled full of patents on generators, motors and electrical transmission systems there were several files on such inventions as a water fountain with 'an unlimited field of use in private dwellings, hotels, theatres, concert halls, hospitals, aquaria and, particularly, in squares, gardens and parks in which it may be carried out on a large scale so as to afford a magnificent spectacle far more captivating and stimulating to the public than the insignificant displays now in use'. There were others for a new type of flying machine, designated a 'helicopter plane', a new type of ship's log, a form of fluid propulsion and ... but why go on? Tesla was clearly a man of immensely fertile imagination and inventive genius. I could so easily lose my way in this mass of patents and inventions. My real task, however, remained. I had to investigate his proposal to broadcast electrical energy without wires.

As I replaced the patents in two large cardboard boxes, I scanned at random the diagrams on the photocopied pages. It suddenly came to me that all along Tesla had been obsessed with the idea of 'wireless' power. Take, for example, that paper on radiant energy. While other scientists had wondered about the exact nature of the Cathode Rays, Tesla immediately saw them in practical terms: since they had the effect of producing electrical charges in matter, he argued, why not use them in place of wires to transmit electrical information?

I hunted through his patents for other hints of his preoccupation with wireless transmission. On November 8, 1898, I discovered, he had been awarded a patent for a 'Method of an Apparatus for Controlling Mechanisms of Moving Vessels or Vehicles' - remote controlled boats, no less.

Tesla had provided drawings of a boat that could be steered at high speed by remote control. He pointed out that previous attempts at remote electrical control made use of wires from ship to shore to carry the electrical messages necessary to control the ship. He proposed something entirely novel:

> I require no intermediate wires, cables, or other form of
> electrical or mechanical connection with the object save
> the natural media in space. I accomplish, nevertheless,
> similar results and in a much more practicable manner by
> producing waves, impulses, or radiations which are
> received through the earth, water, or atmosphere by
> suitable apparatus on the moving body.

What Tesla had designed was a form of radio control as is
made clear by the following sentence from his patent:

> Finally, I may avail myself, in carrying out my invention,
> of electrical oscillations which do not follow any particu-
> lar conducting-path, but propagate in straight lines
> through space, of rays, waves, pulses, or disturbances of
> any kind capable of bringing the mechanism of the mov-
> ing body into action from a distance and at the will of
> the operator by their effect upon suitable controlled
> devices.

Here was the transmission of electricity without wires -
broadcast power. Just a few years after his original invention of
the electrical generator Tesla was working upon devices which
would dispense with the need for connecting cables to transmit
electricity.

I hunted out those patents for the year 1888, with their
diagrams of elegantly simple generators and induction motors
which formed the backbone of the Niagara Falls power project.
By a stroke of genius the young Tesla had thought up a motor
in which the magnetic fields are 'induced' without the need for
direct electrical connections. In a way the motor itself is a
living example of his belief that energy could be transferred
direct, without the need for an intermediary connection.

Yet to draw power from is generators, Tesla needed heavy
electrical cables. When it came to transmitting electrical
current from his power station to a distant town or remote

farmhouse, he was forced to string cables the entire distance.

As I looked at Tesla's drawings I had the illusion that I could see directly into his mind. For a moment I could sense his feeling of irritation with these transmission lines and electrical interconnections. They destroyed the perfection of his scheme. They were ugly intrusions into his otherwise faultless drawings. Tesla, after all, had been able to create light inside glass globes without the need for direct connections of wire. He had shown the world how he could control the movements of a power boat by broadcast signals. Why not a final great achievement, 'Wireless Power' which would unite the earth?

The attractions of this scheme were fairly obvious. Power would be transmitted anywhere in the world. It would be picked up using a simple receiver. Electrical energy could be beamed to large cities, remote settlements, distant islands, and even aeroplanes or ships at sea. The economic implications of a power system which had no need for wires or pylons stretched across fields, up mountains and over rivers, were considerable. Broadcast power could throw the world into an economic revolution with shifts in the traditional power and status of many nations. It was a terrific dream but could the whole thing really work?

The next step was to study a paper written by Tesla in 1904 for a magazine called *Electrical World and Engineer*. In this his first experiments in power transmission were described. The article began with a description of Colorado Springs, the location of his new laboratory. The desert environment seems to have put him in good spirits:

Various reasons, not the least of which was the help proffered by my friend, Leonard E. Curtis, and the Colorado Springs Electric Company, determined me to select for my experimental investigations the large plateau, two thousand metres above sea-level, in the vicinity of that delightful resort, which I reached late in May, 1899. I had not been there but a few days when I congratulated myself on the happy choice and I began the task, for which I had long trained myself, with a grateful sense and full of inspiring hope. The perfect purity of the air, the unequalled beauty of the sky, the imposing sight of a high mountain range, the quiet and restfulness of the place – all around contributed to make the conditions for scientific observation ideal. To this was added the exhilarating influence of a glorious climate and a singular sharpening of the senses. In those regions the organs undergo perceptible physical change. The eyes assume an extraordinary limpidity, improving vision; the ears dry out and become more susceptible to sound. Objects can be clearly distinguished there at distances such that I prefer to have them told by someone else, and I have heard – this I can venture to vouch for – the claps of thunder seven and eight hundred kilometers away. I might have been better still, had it not been tedious to wait for the sounds to arrive, in definite intervals, as heralded precisely by an electrical indicating apparatus- - nearly an hour before.

Tesla quickly assembled his preliminary apparatus and began to investigate electrical fluctuations in the earth itself.

In the middle of June, while preparations for other work were going on, I arranged one of my receiving transformers with the view of determining in a novel manner, experimentally, the electric potential of the globe and studying its periodic and casual fluctuations ... The earth was found to be literally alive with electrical vibrations, and soon I was deeply absorbed in this interesting investigation ... Colorado is a country famous for the natural displays of electric force. In that dry and rarefied atmosphere the sun's rays beat the objects with fierce intensity ... Lightning discharges are, accordingly, very frequent and sometimes of inconceivable violence. On one occasion approximately twelve thousand discharges occurred in two hours, and all in a radius of certainly less than fifty kilometers from my laboratory. Many of them resembled gigantic trees of fire with the trunks up or down.

Later that month Tesla noticed that his instruments recorded strong electrical disturbances associated with storms which were not in the immediate neighbourhood. What could be the cause of such measurements? Tesla was deeply puzzled about the origin of the disturbances and felt himself to be on the edge of 'a great revelation'.

It was on the third of July – the date I shall never forget – when I obtained the first decisive experimental evidence of a truth of overwhelming importance for the advancement of humanity. A dense mass of strongly charged clouds gathered in the west and towards the evening a violent storm broke loose which, after spending much of its fury in the mountains, was driven away with great velocity over the plains. Heavy and long persisting arcs formed almost in regular time intervals. My observations were now greatly facilitated and rendered more accurate by the experiences already gained. I was able to handle my instruments quickly and I was prepared. The recording apparatus being properly adjusted, its indications became fainter and fainter with the increasing distance of the storm, until they ceased altogether. I was watching with eager expectation. Surely enough, in a little while the indications again began, grew stronger and stronger and, after passing through a maximum, gradually decreased and ceased once more. Many times, in regularly recurring intervals, the same actions were repeated until the storm which, as evident from simple computatons, was moving at nearly constant speed had retreated to a distance of three hundred kilometers. Nor did these strange actions stop then, but continued to manifest themselves with undiminished force.

What Tesla seems to be saying is that the earth acted as a giant conductor of electrical signals from the storm and that it continued to conduct the electrical disturbances long after the storm had passed into the distance. It must have been an incredible revelation to discover that the globe itself is an electrical conductor and that the effect of a lightning strike at one location would be to create an electrical impulse which would continue to travel around the world.

Tesla then argued that if impulses from an electrical storm could travel long distances through the earth why should not man-made signals do likewise.

> Impossible as it seemed, this planet, despite its vast extent, behaved like a conductor of limited dimension. The tremendous significance of this fact in the transmission of energy by my system had already become quite clear to me. Not only was it practicable to send telegraphic messages to any distance without wires, as I recognized long ago, but also to impress upon the entire globe the faint modulations of the human voice, far more still to transmit power, in unlimited amounts to any terrestrial distance and almost without any loss.

He poured all his energy into new experiments on the 'Transmission of Electric Energy Without Wires' and made plans for a world-wide power system. Transmission towers would be built all over the world and begin a global system of communication through telegraph and an invention that had all the characteristics of modern radio. This system would also be used to supply homes with electricity. It was part of this original vision that some of this broadcast electrical energy would be produced by the Niagara Power Company for his 'Wireless Transmission'.

> In the first power plant, which I have been designing for a long time, I propose to distribute ten thousand horsepower under a tension of one hundred million volts, which I am now able to produce and handle with safety.

When set beside Tesla's later pronouncements his original

plans for how this electrical energy would be used are curiously modest.

> One of its chief uses will be the illumination of isolated homes ... Another valuable application will be the driving of clocks or such other apparatus ... The idea of impressing upon the earth American time is fascinating and very likely to become popular. There are innumerable devices of all kinds which are either now employed or can be supplied, and by operating them in this manner I may be able to offer a great convenience to the whole world with a plant of no more than ten thousand horse-power.

Tesla stood at the crossroads of our century yet, his considerable imagination and predictive powers notwithstanding, he was unable to foresee the rapid way in which the world would grow dependent on electrical energy. His first plans for Wireless Transmission were predicated upon such modest domestic needs as low power illumination and clocks showing American Time. He had not yet anticipated washers, dryers, dishwashers, refrigerators, ranges, microwave ovens, water heaters or even homes heated by electricity. The average power requirement of a North American home has increased dramatically since Tesla's day. Today a nation's demands for electricity would be far beyond the capacity of a single generating plant. But at the turn of the century Tesla's ideas may not have been all that far-fetched.

Given that the earth behaved like a giant electrical conductor, how did Tesla intend to transmit and distribute this electrical energy from the Niagara Falls power station across the entire globe? He seems to have found a clue in his observations of lightning storms, though he was quick to point out that his method operated in a different way from conventional 'wireless' or radio broadcasting, an approach which Marconi would have been working on at around the same time. The circuit he planned was to be 'the diametrical opposite of a transmitting circuit typical of telegraphy by Hertzian or electromagnetic radiation.'

In a conventional radio broadcasting system, electrical messages are sent through the atmosphere (or through the vacuum of space in the case of communication between rockets or satellites) by means of electromagnetic radiation or Hertzian waves (as Tesla called them). These electromagnetic waves are generated by electrical oscillations pumped into the transmitter. This electrical energy radiates at the speed of light outward in all directions from the transmitter. Radio waves spread out from the transmitter just as sound waves spread from a loudspeaker or ripples expand away from the splash caused by a stone thrown into a pond.

Tesla, however, wrote that his system worked in a very different way from this conventional radio broadcasting.

> The electromagnetic radiations being reduced to an insignificant quantity, and proper conditions of resonance maintained, the circuit acts like an immense pendulum, storing indefinitely the energy of the primary exciting impulses and impressions upon the earth and its conducting atmosphere uniform harmonic oscillations and intensities which, as actual tests have shown, may be pushed so far as to surpass those attained in the natural displays of static electricity.

His idea seemed to be that a transmitter would be used to pump electrical energy into the earth where it would then circulate until it was 'picked up' by a suitable detector.

Chapter Five

AFTER MAKING MY way through his paper, I put Tesla's writings to one side and tried to digest what he had written. I tried to get a feel for what he was attempting, what he had observed and the way he had built up his theory.

I looked at the patent which Tesla had filed on May 16, 1900. It concerned the transmission of electrical energy through 'the Natural Mediums' and contained a description of his energy transmitter, 'the generator which produces stationary waves in the earth.'

A photograph of the Colorado Springs transmitter, which appeared in another publication, shows a tall mast growing from a scaffolding built on the roof of Tesla's laboratory; on the top of the mast is fixed a metal ball.

According to the patent this transmitter was designed to produce oscillations of very high voltage electric current and was not unlike a giant Tesla Coil. High voltage power was first generated in his laboratory by a 'special transformer' or an 'alternating dynamo' and fed into the Primary Coil of the transmitter. This Primary Coil was composed of a few turns of very thick wire and had a low electrical resistance. The Secondary Coil of the apparatus took the form of a spiral of wire, again having low resistance. One end of the wire was earthed and the other attached to the mast with its metal ball.

Tesla emphasized that the geometry of the apparatus should be correct so that certain of its dimensions are in exact ratios to each other. They should also involve precise fractions of the wavelengths of the electrical oscillations to be generated. In this way the Secondary Coil is brought in Resonance with the

Primary Coil and magnification of the 'electrical movement' by many thousands of times becomes possible.

As far as I could see Tesla had designed an enormous electrical circuit which exploited the principle of resonance to step up an applied voltage to many millions of volts. The careful geometry and the resonances of the circuit ensured that these very high voltage currents would oscillate slowly and the maximum voltage output would take place at the metal ball on top of the tower.

The Transmitter was to discharge its electrical energy in such a way that the oscillating currents came in to resonance with the natural electrical oscillations of the earth.

> ... stated otherwise, the terrestrial conductor is thrown into resonance with the oscillations impressed upon it just like a wire ... the planet behaves like a perfectly smooth or polished conductor of inappreciable resistance ... transmitting slow electrical oscillations without sensible distortion or attenuation.

In later patents, Tesla was to introduce modifications and improvements into the design of the transmitter. Patent No. 1, 119, 732 gives some indications of the enormous power he was generating:

> I have shown that it is practicable to produce in resonating circuit EABB'D immense electrical activities, measured by tens and even hundreds of thousands of horse-power and in such a case, if the points of maximum pressure should be shifted below the terminal D, along coil B, *a ball of fire might break out and destroy the support F or anything else in the way.* For the better appreciation of the nature of this danger it should be stated, that the destructive action may take place with inconceivable violence. This will cease to be surprising when it is borne in mind, that the entire energy accumulated in the excited circuit, instead of requiring, as under normal working conditions, one quarter of the period or more for the

transformation from static to kinetic form, may spread itself in an incomparably smaller interval of time, at a rate of many millions of horsepower.

The transmitter was, therefore, to generate hundreds of thousands of horsepower at hundreds of millions of volts. These powerful electrical oscillations were set in resonance with the natural electrical oscillations of the earth and in this way power would be pumped across the globe. The design was staggering. Had Tesla really built such an enormous Magnifying Transmitter and tested it in his Colorado Springs Laboratory? That really would have been something to see!

Later in the day and in a more sober mood I began to consider some practical objections to Tesla's proposal. For all I knew he might well have transmitted power to receivers in the immediate vicinity of his transmitter but that wasn't the same thing as sending energy to the other side of the world.

When it came to Wireless Transmission of Power I had a number of small reservations and one giant objection of principle.

First, the small problems: I had no idea how efficient Tesla's transmitter was, for he provided no figures and no data tables in his patent. I asked myself how much of the energy which Tesla supplied to the Tower was finally converted into the electrical oscillations, for losses of only a few per cent could make the method a poor competitor of conventional Power Line transmission. How much of the original energy supplied was lost in conventional broadcast radiation from the tower, in heating of the coils through electrical resistance, in sparking and other useless processes? Finally, how effective was the resonance between earth and transmitter? Was all the energy in the transmitter transferred to global oscillations? Then what of the receivers themselves? How efficient were they? All these factors seemed to be unknown, a fraction of a per cent here, a few per cent there would soon mount into a fairly inefficient operation. I felt that Tesla was letting me down because he provided no records as to the possible efficiency of his brave new system.

There was a more serious objection and one which would be clear to anyone who has stood beside a pond and thrown small stones into its still water. There is a splash and then ripples expand outward in the form of concentric circles. At first these ripples are quite noticeable, but the further away they move from the centre of the splash, the smaller they become. The reason is obvious. As the stone is thrown into the water a certain amount of energy is released which produces a strong local disturbance – a splash. The energy then radiates outward but the further it moves the more 'spread out' it becomes. In other words, this energy must be distributed over a bigger and bigger volume.

The energy from the explosion of a grenade, sound from a loudspeaker, electromagnetic radiation from a radio mast, light from the sun, all are governed by the same principle that the further the energy expands from the source the weaker its density will be.

The same objection applies to Tesla's power transmission. Close to the transmitter the energy available is very large but as it spread out further and further – over tens or hundreds of miles – the energy in any particular area becomes smaller and smaller.

Power requirements of a modern home or office are measured in thousands of watts. This would mean that a 'roof top' power receiver on each building would need to be capable of picking up hundreds or thousands of watts on a continuous basis. The power available in each few square feet of ground far from the transmitter would, therefore, have to be high. And this would have to be true for every few square feet of ground over the whole world. The conclusion is simple: to provide the power requirement for the average home, the energy pumped out from a Tesla Transmitter would need to be almost astronomical.

By contrast a conventional power transmission line delivers energy exactly where it is required. The transmission line loses a small percentage of the electricity through resistance but at least it brings the power direct to each home or factory and does not spread it out over an enormous area.

A simple analogy may serve to illustrate this point. A farmer, who has read a great deal about the Tesla Transmitter, tries to irrigate his farm by Broadcast Power. He requires several fields to be irrigated that are scattered over an area which includes several roads, a small wood and some farm buildings. Above his well which produces a certain number of gallons per hour, he erects a tower and sprays water from it at high velocity.

Around the tower everything looks fine, the earth is moist and the corn green and well advanced. As he takes a walk to his other fields he discovers his mistake. To begin with, all his farm buildings are flooded. The water has fallen everywhere: on fields, woods, buildings and roads. When he reaches his furthest fields, he finds that they are bone dry - for only the finest spray of water has reached them. The problem is obvious, the further the water has to travel, the greater area it must cover and the less water is available per acre.

The disillusioned farmer now goes back to his old method of digging ditches. Although is hard work he is at least able to conduct the water exactly where it is needed. He is able to control the amount of water he needs in each field. The farmer realises that he will lose a little water through seepage in each of the ditches, but when it comes to the furthest fields the old fashioned technique is far more efficient.

That seemed to be that. I could see in a way that when the average home needed only a few watts of power to run an electric clock or a small light, Tesla's Magnifying Transmitter did not seem all that crazy. But for today? Tesla just hadn't convinced me. To begin with, the notes I had before me were far too brief. I had no idea how efficient his system of power generation would be. More seriously, the millions of horsepower which were pumped from his transmitter would spread all over the globe. By the time they reached the nearest town the energy which could be picked up from a roof-top receiver would barely light a torch battery. As far as I could see, Tesla's Power Transmission was dead and buried.

Chapter Six

MY CONCLUSIONS ABOUT Power Transmission caused my interest to falter. I felt I had read too much about Nikola Tesla and badly wanted to get back to my old routine. But he would not lie down so easily; after a day my mood of listlessness faded and, picking up one of the biographies, I began to read.

Nikola Tesla was born on July 9, 1856, in the village of Smiljan, Croatia. The year of his birth was shared with Freud, Woodrow Wilson, Oscar Wilde and Bernard Shaw. In the same year, Burton and Speke set out to find the source of the Nile, the Treaty of Paris brought the Crimean War to an end and James Buchanan was elected President of the United States.

Few of these events would have reached the ears of Tesla's father, Milutin, who acted as pastor in the Serbian Orthodox Church, or to his mother, Djouka, who could not even read although she possessed the gift of languages.

The family consisted of five children and for the first years of his life the sickly, introspective Nikola lived under the shadow of an older brother Dane.

Dane, seven years older than Nikola, was considered by the family to be their greatest gift - a genius: so it was particularly tragic when he suffered a serious fall. The boy lay ill for several days and Tesla was moved to a neighbour's house, for there were rumours that he had pushed his elder brother down the cellar steps.

Dane died and in Nikola was born the determination to excel the genius of his departed brother. Such a burden can become unbearable to a sensitive child. Another pastor's son, Vincent Van Gogh, grew up in the shadow of a dead brother, also named Vincent, who had been destined for great things. In his psychological study of the painter, *Stranger on the Earth*, A. J. Lubin tells how this brother became an obsession in Van Gogh's life which he attempted to work out through the many images of death and resurrection which occur in his paintings.

In his autobiography *The Secret Life of Salvador Dali*, the Catalan painter writes of his brother, also named Salvador, who died before Dali was born:

> He had the unmistakable facial morphology of a genius … I, on the other hand, was much less intelligent, but I reflected everything.

Dali also claims that in being christened in the name of his dead brother, he became the 'saviour' of modern painting.

Nikola appears to have been a thin, unhealthy boy, very shy and a worry to his parents. His major love was nature and for hours he would walk in the countryside and imagine how he could harness the power of the wind or the endless movement of the rivers. In this, young Nikola was following in his mother's footsteps, for Djouka was famed for her household inventions and labour saving devices. For the time being, the future electrical genius contented himself by building tiny waterwheels and a motor powered by June bugs.

When Nikola was seven the family moved to the larger town of Gospic where he attended school until, as a young adolescent, he was sent to a higher school at Carlstadt, Croatia. The boy was a good pupil, excelling in retaining mathematical formulae in his head. His enthusiasm for the new science of electricity was so strong that he taught himself English in order to read Edison's papers.

Tesla's self-imposed struggle towards genius took a new turn when he apparently made the conscious decision to grow into a pure intellect. At some point in his teens he began to distrust emotion and to argue that it hindered true intellectual development. From that time on, Nikola Tesla seems to have trained himself to suppress all emotion and feeling and to avoid the closer forms of human contact. If he was to grow into a superman then it would be by pure reason alone.

As Nikola neared the end of his school life, military service loomed ahead. The Tesla legend has it that the boy deliberately contracted cholera and became seriously ill in order to avoid being drafted. This is certainly a dramatic story but how much truth is there in it? As an adult, Tesla wrote part of his autobiography and was given to all manner of pronouncements in the newspapers and magazines. Much of what I read remained elusive, the kernel of truth missing or obscured by excessive claims and predictions. Tesla the man seems as difficult to pin down as do his ideas and, on many occasions, I find myself questioning incidents from his life. Were all the stories strictly true, had they been embellished in the telling or had they been invented, even by Tesla himself, as a means of obscuring the truth?

No matter what the origin of Tesla's illness, he certainly avoided military service and found himself instead at the Polytechnic in Graz, Austria. There he came under the influence of a physics teacher, Professor Poeschl, who introduced him to the invention of Zénobe Théophile Gramme.

In 1871, Gramme had demonstrated a new direct current dynamo which came to be known as the Gramme motor. Although other motors had been built before Gramme's, his was the first to possess commercial possibilities. Two years later, as Tesla joined the Polytechnic, Gramme's motor was shown at the Vienna Exhibition. It was then realized that not only could the device be used to generate electricity but, if supplied with external electrical power, it would act as a motor and could then be used to drive machines.

Faced with this miraculous new invention the teenage student was far from impressed. To begin with, Tesla pointed to the commutator or mechanical connection used to conduct electricity between the fixed and moving parts of the Gramme motor. Nikola argued with his professor that the machine was inefficient and lost power through sparking at the commutator when run at high speed.

For his part the perceptive Professor Proschl issued Tesla a challenge which was to preoccupy him over the next two years. If Gramme's machine was so poor, then could the student invent a better one? Tesla took up the glove Poeschl had thrown down and replied that he would devise a machine that worked with alternating, in place of direct, current.

Prague University replaced Graz Polytechnic and the teenager grew into a tall and strikingly handsome young man. His confidence seems to have developed about this time and after leaving university he became manager of a telephone office in Budapest responsible for installing new machinery. His inventive genius received its first reward at this time with the granting of a patent for a telephone amplifier.

The idea of a new and improved electric motor continued to nag at him and, early in 1882, he contracted a minor illness and spent a few days off work. His young assistant, Szigeti, stopped by and suggested that they should walk together in the park. The two friends strolled along admiring the sunset which inspired Nikola to recite from Goethe. Suddenly, the young man stopped as if paralyzed. Tesla describes in his own words what happened next:

> When in a moment of inspiration I was pronouncing these words, the idea occurred to me like a flash of lightning and in a second the truth revealed itself. With a stick I drew in the sand the diagrams ...

At that instant Tesla had conceived the plans of an induction motor, a motor upon which all modern electrical generating systems would rely and which, one day, would find its way into a host of electrical devices.

Inventing a new device is one thing, financing its development and marketing is another. Tesla moved to Paris and the Continental Edison Company where, in a fever, he drafted new designs for motors, generators and transformers. In those early days he created out of his own head all the components of our present day electrical transmission systems, yet no one seemed interested.

Tesla looked in vain for someone who would finance his

ambitious plans, then in despair he cashed his final savings and booked passage on the steam ship *Saturnia*. Nikola Tesla had decided, in 1884, that he must go right to the top. He would sail to New York and talk with the only man who could understand the importance of his invention, Thomas Alva Edison.

Chapter Seven

THE FOLLOWING MORNING was one of those when I took my time getting dressed. As a scientist, I had long ago learned to trust that desire to daydream so I made no attempt to hurry to work. When the mind wanders without any conscious attempt at control, day dreams can lead to hunches and intuitions, and often occur along the pathway to some new scientific insight.

That morning I found myself recalling Tesla's enthusiasm about his experiments at Colorado Springs. He had been fired by a vision of worldwide power transmission and he believed that broadcast power was an utterly practical possibility.

I began to think of the very obvious objections I could raise against Tesla's system. Any scientist would have been struck by the same point, that if energy is broadcast across the globe, it will be spread so thin as to be of no practical use in powering machinery, heating homes, supplying cooking ranges and any of the thousand and one other jobs electricity is used for.

Yet something was nagging me. Of course, the point was totally obvious, for the very same objections I had made must have been known to Tesla himself. Yet in spite of this he had gone on to build a second tower, this time on Long Island.

I began to wonder if Nikola Tesla had made fools out of all of us. He had been at pains to point out that his invention was very different from conventional broadcasting using 'Herzian waves'. Was Tesla Transmission based upon some totally new principle? Had he perhaps discovered a way to beam energy directly to a given target without dissipating its power over a wide area?

I switched on the radio and another thought struck me. Here I was with an expensive stereo set, one of the few luxuries I could afford, full of transistors, printed circuits and the like. I could walk in to any electronics shop and buy kits containing all manner of exotic things like digital counters, oscilloscopes, microprocessors, memory circuits and high speed measuring devices. These were standard equipment in every physicist's laboratory and now within the price range of any enthusiastic amateur. The point was that none of this equipment would have been available to Nikola Tesla.

At Colorado Springs the great inventor was denied the high speed electronics which our modern age takes for granted. By contrast his own equipment must have been crude and fairly insensitive. Yet Tesla claimed to have sent bursts of electrical power through the earth and to have detected and measured the returning signal.

Electrical power moving at the speed of light could circumnavigate the globe in a tiny fraction of a second. How then had Tesla been able to measure such time intervals with any accuracy? Was the returning signal really a wave which had been reflected from the antipodes or simply some local power surge produced in his own laboratory?

I thought yet again how the Tesla story had so many different faces. The man and his experiments were so hard to pin down: each time I felt that the book on Nikola Tesla was about to close, a new chapter would open up. This time it involved the laboratory he had built. With all that massive equipment around, it seemed perfectly possible that once the Tesla Transmitter was in action some transients may have occurred. Following each burst of power from the transmitter, smaller transient current flows may have been registered in the laboratory. Possibly, in his enthusiasm, Tesla then took these readings as evidence that his power pulses had travelled around the earth and returned with undiminished power.

When I reached my office later that morning, the secretary told me that a Dr. Microwski had been trying to reach me. Since Andrew Microwski was a member of P.A.C.E., I called back at once and after a short chat over the phone we agreed to meet for lunch at the end of the week. I told him that I was keen to talk about Tesla and find out exactly what happened at Colorado Springs.

Just as I was putting the phone down, one of my colleagues put his face round the door.

'Hey, what've you been doing all these weeks? I thought you were dead.'

I shrugged my shoulders.

'Let's go for a coffee', he suggested.

My friend shouted down the corridor to a couple of his friends and together we all walked to the cafeteria.

After a little joking, they began to question my preoccupation over the last weeks. My explanations were greeted with laughter.

'So that's it, you're personal advisor to the Prime Minister now?'

'Are you going to make a fortune erecting Tesla Towers across Canada?'

'I know – you're president of the world centre for occult science'.

'Send a crank to catch a crank.'

I joined in their laughter but I did not feel ready to explain myself. The topic eventually became exhausted and as the cafeteria began to empty our conversation drifted to other things.

Eventually there were only two of us left at the table and as I made a movement to leave my companion suddenly began to speak quite seriously.

'You know I've read all about this radio interference.'

I must have looked surprised for he began to explain himself. He told me that, although he did not have a scientific background like the others, he was very interested in what I was doing. My friend had a short wave radio of his own and several months ago had noticed curious interference. 'What do you think of it all,' he asked, 'have the Russians really built a Tesla transmitter?'

'There are several possibilities which could account for the interference,' I explained. 'Most people seem to think that it's a new form of radar.'

'So you don't really think there's anything in Power Transmissions?' he asked me.

I hesitated a moment. 'Well, that's what I'm trying to find out but it's not that easy. You see it all happened so long ago that I don't really know what actually took place. Tesla said that he could transmit power without loss and he hinted at an inexhaustible source of power.'

'Do you think it's possible?' my friend asked.

'Not in any conventional sort of way,' I replied. 'The question is: did he do something new? There's not much to go on and what I've read is terribly vague.'

I stopped and began to play with my cup. Across the table my friend smiled. 'I think that Schneider picked the right man. He's no fool.'

I was surprised. 'What do you mean?'

'Well, he knew that you wouldn't give up so easily. You'd keep at it, just in case there's anything in it.'

I tried not to smile, it was a compliment which I was sure was unjustified. 'You've got to realize that any research organization gets all sorts of cranky ideas,' I told him. 'People keep writing in with plans for crazy machines and new theories. They either want money or they'd like you to build the invention and test it for them. There just isn't enough time in a day to take it all seriously.'

'But Tesla wasn't that sort of a crank, was he? He made some very clever inventions.'

I began to flounder. 'Well, I don't know. Maybe he ended up as a crank ... some of his later ideas ... I just don't know.'

My friend pressed on. 'Some people would say that you've had pretty far out ideas yourself; stuff on Black Holes, time going backwards, all that sort of thing. Don't they sound crazy too?'

'All right, you win,' I began to laugh. 'If Tesla isn't a crank, then I suppose that he must have invented something very special. He talks about sending power right through the earth and at other times, he says that he's using the voltage difference between the earth and the upper atmosphere.'

'But could he really have discovered something?'

'No. I don't really think so – but I did wonder if he'd found some way to develop a self-contained beam ... no, I don't think it's possible.' I paused and began to think aloud. 'Some sort of plasma beam which could link the transmitter and receiver.'

My friend's face began to light up as I talked and I wondered why. In the end I asked him if it was important to him that Tesla had been right.

'Well, I'm not a scientist but I read a lot. There are so many things we don't understand. Things that science won't talk about, they're all pushed under the carpet ... take flying saucers for example.'

I took a guess at what he was trying to say. 'You mean that you've got a feeling that science has left something out? That there's something important about the world and science never includes it?'

He thought for a little, then began to speak again. 'I don't know if I'd put it that way but maybe you're right. Sometimes scientists seem too clever – you see them on television and they talk about the world and how everything can be explained. But there are other things like E.S.P. and flying saucers and now there's your Tesla business, and all they do is laugh at it.'

'I think you're dissatisfied at the scientific picture of nature,' I suggested and then realized that I too was trying to laugh off his suggestion. 'Maybe there should be something more. Could we really have left out something?'

He smiled back at me. 'I don't know. But I'm interested in what you're doing with Tesla. This new power he talks about, out of the air. You said it's got something to do with high voltages, could it be the same thing as thunderstorms?'

I shook my head. 'No, I don't think so. You're right that thunderstorms are electrical and they do contain a great deal of energy, but I don't think Tesla had them in mind. You get thunderstorms in the lower part of the atmosphere and he talks about the upper atmosphere as the source. You see, thunder-storms occur as air currents build up electrical charges on thunderclouds. The air rubs together, it's the same thing that happens when you rub your feet on a nylon carpet. In the end you build up a big electrical charge. In a thundercloud, it gets up to several million volts, and when the atmosphere is full of rain, the whole thing begins to discharge as big electrical sparks. A thunderstorm certainly has a lot of power but it's not fixed in one place and it depends on so many atmospheric factors. It's just too unpredictable to be Tesla's mysterious power source.'

'Well, go on,' my friend encouraged.

'I've been wondering if the Power Transmission bit could have some connection with electrical layers in the upper atmosphere. You know, the particle belts around the earth. I wonder if they could be used to focus Energy Transmission?'

'What are you going to do about it?'

I thought for a moment. 'I suppose I'm going to try and find out.'

A few hours later I was at the Herzberg Institute of Astrophysics finding out about the electrically charged layers which are situated about the earth. I was talking to one of the scientists and had asked him to go fairly slowly.

'Let's look at it this way,' he began. 'The sunshine you get at the seaside may seem pretty strong but you've got to remember that it is passed all the way through our atmosphere and the most powerful wavelengths have been filtered out by the time it reaches the ground. Pure unfiltered sunlight, the sort of thing which hits the upper atmosphere, contains X-rays and ultra-violet light. It's got so much energy that it can break up the molecules of oxygen and nitrogen in the air. What happens is that the molecules absorb so much light-energy that internal stresses tear them apart into electrically charged atoms and electrons.'

He drew some equations on a piece of paper to demonstrate the processes involved.

'If you send a rocket high into the atmosphere,' he continued, 'it registers an increasing number of charged particles or ions. You get oxygen and nitrogen ions, ozone and even free electrons. If you go right to the outer limits of the atmosphere you meet protons and other particles which stream out from the sun and across space to the earth.'

'I can remember most of that from my university physics,' I said. 'The X-rays and ultraviolet light from the sun ionize the upper atmosphere.'

'Yes, but there's another important factor. The earth acts like a big magnet with a pole at the top and bottom – the North and South poles. The charged particles in the upper atmosphere tend to run along the magnetic lines of force and form charged bands or layers around the earth.'

'A bit like a magnetic tunnel?' I asked.

'Yes, the charged particles spiral along the magnetic lines of force in definite layers. For a time they get trapped but even when they escape there are always new particles waiting to take their place.'

'So these particles move thousands of miles around the earth on definite paths? The effect must be something like huge electrical currents in the upper atmosphere.' I felt I should explain the reason for my visit. 'You see, all this interests me because I'm investigating a proposal made by Nikola Tesla.'

I explained how Tesla had built an electrical machine which resonated at very high voltages and great power. The machine was supposed to broadcast electrical power across the earth and Tesla claimed that his signals had been transmitted right across the earth without any loss.

'That couldn't be possible,' my colleague objected. 'Any form of broadcasting would be very inefficient. The signal would simply spread out.'

I nodded to him and continued. 'I know, but I'm trying to see if there could be some way to confine and guide the energy in a narrow beam. I'm just making wild guesses. You see, we've only got Tesla's word that the thing worked and it all happened so long ago.'

'Are you asking me if there could be some sort of wave-guide in the upper atmosphere. A way of keeping the energy from spreading outward?'

'Yes,' I replied. 'Sometimes Tesla talked about sending the power *through* the earth but he also mentioned the voltage difference between earth and the upper atmosphere. Could there be some way of using these charged layers? I mean, would it be possible to induce a sort of wave-guide between the transmitter and receiver?'

Across the table the astrophysicist began to squirm a little as he sketched a doodle in front of him. 'No, I don't like it. You're talking about sending a great deal of power on a continuous basis; pumping energy thousands of miles in some sort of magnetic tunnel. These charged layers depend on a very delicate equilibrium. The number of ions in the upper atmosphere could fluctuate. You get magnetic storms on the sun which have a big effect on the upper atmosphere. I really don't see how you could ever send large amounts of power in this way – even if it were possible, I don't see how it could be more efficient than conventional transmission cables.'

I looked at him for a while. 'Then you're sceptical?' I asked.

'Definitely,' he said.

I thanked him, took the equations and sketches he had made and began to get up from the table. He looked up and hesitated for a moment.

'There is something which may interest you.'

'Yes,' I said.

'You may have read about it in one of the scientific magazines. It is a very interesting effect.'

'Go on,' I encouraged, 'tell me about it.'

'Well, some experiments on one of the charged layers showed that it was oscillating at sixty times a second.'

'Really,' I said.

'Well, what else oscillates sixty times a second?'

'Ordinary electrical current – power lines' I said.

'That's it. It turned out that these oscillations were caused by the power lines which are stretched across the Province of Quebec. They carry high voltage current at sixty cycles a second. It seems that this is enough to induce similar oscillations in the charged layers in the upper atmosphere.'

'So if someone built a Tesla Tower and operated it with a great deal of high voltage current – if they pumped out enough power – then it would pulse the particle layers in the upper atmosphere?' I asked.

'Well, I suppose it's possible. Yes, I think it could happen. But to go from there to a waveguide which allows tremendous power to be transmitted without loss, well that's far too big a jump.'

Chapter Eight

AFTER MY VISIT to the Herzberg Institute I continued biographical reading in an attempt to form a picture of Tesla and the way he worked at Colorado Springs. But as I went deeper into the biographies I realized that Tesla was still an enigma. The books mentioned incidents from his childhood and reported youthful conversations, but I began to ask myself: had all this actually happened? How had the biographer obtained such information? Was it a report at first hand or had it been filtered through decades of recollection and retelling? Had all the anecdotes been woven together by friends and relatives to make a 'good story'?

Tesla as a boy was supposed to have been interested in machines and to have constructed ingenious inventions for his mother. But many children pass through such periods of model building and the results are acclaimed with pride by their parents; I had the cynical feeling that if Tesla had become a writer or a composer there would have been legends concerning infant story telling or rapt attention to the church organ.

As I read about Tesla's youth one remark stands out strongly. It was the suggestion that Tesla was able to receive the plans and designs for his inventions in a very direct way, right into his imagination. Even the originals of the complicated electrical machines he was later to invent appear to have been received in a flash. A device, in all its detail, would miraculously appear in his mind and he would then begin to construct the working apparatus simply by copying the design from his imagination.

An inventor is generally thought to spend a great deal of time in developing his invention. Plans are redrawn, scale models built, components modified and at times drastic redesigning is needed. The final working version evolves through a long process of calculation, experimentation and revision. But in Tesla's case each invention is supposed to have appeared as fully formed visions, already refined and without the need for further experimentation.

The curious nature of Tesla's visions interested me a great deal. I had always been fascinated by the creative process and by the way an idea is generated and perfected. But I was also cautious as to how much truth there was in this story of plans appearing directly in Tesla's mind. Could the story be a romantic elaboration on the part of Tesla's friends or even a piece of mystification created by Tesla himself?

Other scientists and artists had left accounts of the flash of insight which occurs in the calm, relaxed moments following a period of concentration on a particular problem. Although the creative breakthrough may seem to occur in an instant, it is always preceded by weeks or months of hard work which at the time had seemed to produce little result. Yet even after the greatest flashes of genius, hard work must follow before the idea can grow to practical form. Details have to be worked out and different techniques tried. Often the creative flash is not so much the solution to a problem as a new way of seeing things. Armed with a new perception, the old difficulties are swept away. But in all the other cases I had read about, hard work separated the initial insight from its final goal.

In Tesla's case a more dramatic process seems to have occurred; but again I found myself wishing for more concrete evidence as to the many claims made about Tesla and his achievements.

Further reading helped me to realize that there was a connecting thread in Tesla's nature which began in his teens when he spoke of dedicating his life to science and using reason and imagination to improve the world. I reflected that it is not unusual for a young person to give his life to a consuming idea. It could be poetry, sport, religion, even hedonism. Anything which an individual can embrace with his whole energy so that it gives a sense of meaning to his life. The romantic poets of the nineteenth century, for example, had been willing to give their lives for the refinement of experience and the intoxication of their senses.

Tesla seemed to be of the same mould as these poets, but in his case it involved a dedication to science. In arriving at his decision, however, Tesla felt it necessary to cut away what he saw as the weakness in his nature. He resolved to drive himself through pure reason and leave feeling and emotion by the wayside. In fact, his ideal was the man-machine, an efficient intellect whose judgements would be made without interference by fickle emotion.

I soon realized that this was much more than a passing adolescent whim. Tesla had determined his future as surely as if he had dedicated himself to the intoxication of his senses through opium. He believed that reason and emotion stood in opposition and he pictured emotion as subtracting from logic and diluting the life of reason. His solution, therefore, was to dominate and control his feelings through the power of his intellect. For Tesla the superman must castrate his emotions to leave a mind at peace with logic.

There is terrible danger inherent in such a plan. For a number of years I had been interested in the writings of the Swiss Analytic-Psychologist Carl Jung. Jung, too, had considered various aspects of personality as being in opposition, but his conclusions were very different from Tesla's. Jung believed that each of these opposing components must balance. The well rounded person would have emotion complemented by reason and intellect in harmony with feelings. Mental health involves a continued equilibrium between these aspects which give power and health to the personality.

Jung had warned of the dangers to a personality which is out of balance through the dominance of one of these components. If an aspect of personality is buried, then disaster will follow, since no part of a human can be buried without psychic sacrifice. If reason is forced to dominate, then its frustrated hidden brother, emotion, works underground. Feelings which have long been denied grow in power and seek new ways to restore their balance. Eruptions of emotion from the shadow world of the mind are sensed as a threat by reason, which struggles even harder to maintain control. In the end an unexpected chink in the armour of reason is uncovered and through this fissure uncontrolled feelings in all their naked power gush out.

Since Tesla attempted to suppress a part of his essential self, he stood in danger of being overwhelmed and controlled by that very power he sought to deny. I began to wonder how this had affected Tesla's life. I knew of no major breakdown in his life. Had repressed emotion perhaps used more subtle means? Was it stretching the imagination too much to wonder if it had worked in an ironic way by subverting reason to its own ends?

If I followed the whole thing to its logical conclusion, then I would see Tesla's life as the story of a man obsessed with the desire to control the naked forces of nature. He struggled to tame electricity, at that time an unknown and powerful force. Did this desire to exercise control over electrical power come from the same origin as his need to control his own inner nature? Had his life's work become a metaphor for the need to control the emotional forces within his own body? I realized that my arguments were becoming a little far fetched but I couldn't help wondering if Tesla had been guilty of an inner blindness, a final act of treason on the part of his critical power when it came to his dream of Broadcast Power.

Reflections such as these occupied me for the next few days until the morning I was to meet Andrew Microwski for lunch. My trip downtown took less time than I had expected and I arrived at our meeting place only to discover that the restaurant was not due to open for another five minutes.

We had agreed to eat in a café located inside the city's theatre complex. From its windows, we would be able to look out at the frozen canal which was filled with skaters at lunch time. As I had several minutes to wait, I strolled over to a comfortable armchair located in the foyer and sat down.

I had no idea of Microwski's age or his appearance, so I decided to play the game I had invented while waiting in an airport lounge on the way to an important scientific conference. I used to sit watching the various arrivals and try to guess which of them could be a scientist. In the past, my success rate had been exceptionally high.

This time the target was a member of P.A.C.E. and I scanned the group standing outside the café for possible candidates. After a few moments the café opened and this seemed to trigger a fresh influx of people. One of them strode forward in an ill fitting coat, his oversized snow boots flapping about his heels. Without doubt, here was an eccentric and dedicated scientist. I stood up and held out my hand to Dr. Microwski. At the same moment, I felt someone clap me on the shoulder and spun round to face a heavily built young man.

'Dr. David Peat?' he asked. 'I spotted you, I'm Andrew Microwski. Can I help you?'

Andrew was a cheerful and enthusiastic man, neat and with a slight foreign accent and exceptional confidence. He guided me into the restaurant and claimed a table near the window. Dr. Microwski was not the man to bother with the formalities of conversation; as soon as we had ordered our meal he plunged straight into business.

'Now, how can we help you, Dr. Peat?'

Before I had time to reply he had begun to talk in an animated way about Tesla's inventions and the hope they offered to a world deep in the grips of an energy crisis. I felt disoriented by the force and direction of his conversation and tried to explain that I was only just finding my own way through Tesla's writings.

'What I'm trying to do,' I said, 'is attempt to understand Tesla Power Transmission.'

'I know all that, Dr. Peat,' Andrew replied. 'I've talked to Dr. Schneider, your president, on the telephone. You see we have a large amount of information on Tesla. Is there any way we can help you?'

I told him that I had really hoped for a relaxed chat over lunch so that we could get to know each other a little. I also wanted to know a little more about P.A.C.E. But Andrew Microwski had no wish to pussyfoot where Tesla was concerned. He continued in full force.

'Do you realize that there are eminent scientists in the

United States who are very interested in Tesla's work and feel
that it should be investigated?'

I soon realized that Andrew was totally dedicated to Tesla
and his visions. As to the predictions, he took them all quite
literally. Over our meal he emphasized the importance of
various inventions and told me that so many of them were
ahead of their time that they had been ignored by orthodox
scientists. In the face of so much compelling enthusiasm I
simply sat back, listened and enjoyed the meal. Although I did
not say so, I felt that some of his statements should be taken
with a generous pinch of salt. In particular, I was worried
about all those claims made on behalf of eminent scientists
who, he said, were enthusiastic about power transmission or
were already investigating the theory. When I later got around
to contacting several of them over the telephone, it appeared
that in many cases Andrew's reports had been considerably
exaggerated. Yet for all that, I could not be angry with him;
compared with the cautious and the calculating, Andrew
Microwski was bubbling with life.

As we relaxed after our meal, Andrew began to tell me about
his concern about the world's weather. He claimed that Russian
scientists had built a Tesla Transmitter and were using it to
modify weather on a global scale. He even hinted that various
intelligence agencies in Canada and the United States knew
about these experiments and had begun to tabulate data on
recent dramatic changes in storm centres, rainfall and winds.

I was not sure how to react to all this. After all, I was no
expert on the weather: most of my knowledge came from the
pages in popular science magazines; but as far as I could
remember there had been no reports of dramatic changes in the
world's weather over the last few months. The best I could do
would be to make a few phone calls to the weather experts and
learn their opinions. As far as Andrew was concerned,
however, North America's weather had definitely changed for
the worse and it was all due to Tesla Transmitters outside
Riga.

Over our coffee, I steered Andrew back to the topic of power
transmission. I told him that I was having some difficulty in

understanding Tesla and was worried by the lack of any hard evidence to back his claims.

'You've read about Tesla's experiments at Colorado Springs? He sent power around the earth faster than the speed of light,' Andrew said.

'Yes, I know he says that. But what worries me is that it isn't very scientific, I mean he doesn't give much in the way of details.'

'But many scientists have studied Tesla's work,' Andrew went on. 'They are building Tesla transmitters all over¡ the world. A young engineer named Tim Richardson is building a transmitter right here in Canada, at Timmins, Ontario. He will be able to transmit power to groups in the United States.'

This was an exciting piece of news. As far as I could see a little hard data was worth several volumes of predictions and speculations. 'Thanks, that's really interesting,' I said. 'Can you let me have Richardson's address and phone number?'

'Certainly. We've got a great deal of information for you if you'd only ask. Did you know that Dr. Arthur Matthews, who is living near Quebec City, helped Tesla with many of his experiments? The American Air Force is also very interested in Tesla.'

I tried to steer the conversation back to the Transmitter. 'I'm having quite a problem with some of Tesla's writings. I'm not sure if I always understand what he's getting at.'

'But it's all explained in a paper written by Dr. Puharich. Puharich has made a very long study of all the writings and patents.'

'It's really Tesla's own writings that worry me, they're so brief and I can't get enough detail out of them.'

'What do you mean?' Andrew asked.

'Well, in most scientific reports there's a lot of detail, with tabulations of experimental results, derivation of formulae and that sort of thing. It means that you can always go back and check to see exactly what was done. You really can't do that with Tesla.'

Andrew smiled at me. 'You have to read Tesla very carefully, Dr. Peat. Everything in the writings is very helpful.

When you study his work you'll find a little sentence that you don't understand at first so it sends you back to something else. Very slowly you'll begin to understand what he was getting at. We've studied Tesla's writings for several years so if you want to know anything just ask.'

'Well, I may have to do that one day. Thank you.'

Andrew smiled at me again. 'You must look very deep. Did you know that the patents are written so carefully that you have to follow them to the letter, otherwise the device won't work.'

I joked that it sounded a little like a soufflé recipe, but Andrew did not laugh.

'I'm serious, Dr. Peat. When Tim Richardson tried to build his Transmitter at Timmins, he found that he had to follow the patent exactly.' Andrew paused and looked at me, 'This is a whole new technology we're offering you. It was discovered by Tesla many years ago but it's a whole new technology.'

He was very serious for a moment, then his face broke out into a huge smile. It was time for both of us to leave. I told Andrew that I'd enjoyed our conversation and that I would probably be in touch again.

As we walked out of the restaurant Andrew clasped me on the shoulder again: 'Don't forget, study his writings, everything there, all his inventions, radio, superconductivity, incredible machines. He discovered a source of cosmic power, we're offering it to you – an inexhaustible source of energy.'

Chapter Nine

TIM RICHARDSON, the Canadian who was building a Tesla transmitter, proved to be a difficult man to trace. It took a long series of calls before I eventually contacted him one afternoon. At first Richardson was reluctant to talk about his research and I suspected that he had been pestered by cranks and people trying to exploit his ideas. But as we began to discuss Tesla's patents he relaxed and told me that he was building a transmitter according to the plans left by Tesla. As far as I could make out the project had been funded by several local businessmen and was being completed in Tim Richardson's spare time.

I asked him how work was progressing.

'There are a lot of problems,' he told me. 'It has to be built according to Tesla's patents – we need exactly the right thickness of wire, all that sort of thing.'

'Are there any other scientists working on it with you?' I asked.

'No, but I did talk to a professor at the University of Toronto. He gave me some help with the design.'

There was something else which interested me about these activities in Timmins. 'How did you get on to Tesla in the first place? To tell you the truth I'd never heard of him until I got involved through writing this report.'

'I've always been interested in electrical experiments and I first read some of Tesla's patents a long time ago. It got me fascinated – all those inventions. A bit later I worked with a man called Golka in the States.'

'What does he do?' I asked.

'He's built something like a Tesla tower. It operates at several million volts.'

This last piece of news was quite a surprise. I had no idea that anyone else had gone so far as to actually build one of Tesla's gigantic coils.

'You mean he's actually got a Tesla Transmission Tower working?'

'Yes, but I think it may be a secret. He has something to do with the American Air Force.'

I began to wonder if Andrew had been right after all about international interest in Tesla. We discussed several more details about the transmitter before I came to my final question.

'There's one thing I'd like to know, Tim. Did you build this tower so that you could transmit power? What do you think of Power Transmission?'

Tim Richardson was silent for a moment.

'Tesla claimed that he'd done that at Colorado Springs. He said a lot of things and so many of them were right and ahead of his time.... But ... I don't really know. I'm going to try some experiments along that line but I don't know if they will work. The reason I'm building the Tower is to study how it works and to try to produce very high voltages.'

Tim Richardson, a fairly level headed man, was open minded about Tesla's theories. I realized that his experiments at Timmins could be valuable. I wished him the best of luck with his transmitter and asked him to keep me in touch with the progress of work.

I looked at my watch and saw that it was close to four in the afternoon. I had been very intrigued by Tim's mention of a Tesla Tower which had something to do with the U.S. Air Force. Would it be possible to trace this Dr. Golka in what remained of the afternoon? I had very little to go on, simply a name and connection with the Air Force. I began with Directory Enquiries for New York, Boston and Washington. After some juggling with all the Golkas in those cities, I began to trace the relatives of the man I wanted and a little later the telephone number of the scientist himself, located at Wendover Airforce Base.

The final telephone call connected me with Dr. Golka and

'Project Tesla' at the Air Base. It turned out that Dr. Golka was even more reluctant to talk to me than Tim Richardson had been. He was particularly worried about any publicity for his project and told me that he wanted to avoid getting pestered by cranks.

In the end Dr. Golka confirmed that he had built a Tesla Transformer capable of generating 20 million volts. The device operated in short bursts at 2,200 amps and the coils resonated at two frequencies simultaneously.

I asked Golka what was the purpose of the tower. Did the Air Force have an interest in power transmission, for example? He refused to be drawn on the topic of power transmission beyond the fact that the explanations put forward by Tesla himself seemed incorrect. He said that the Tower at Wendover had been built to generate very high voltages for a series of experiments. Project Tesla was in fact an investigation of stable plasmas and Ball Lightning.

The idea of experiments on Ball Lightning struck me as ironic. Ten or twenty years earlier Dr. Golka himself would have been dubbed a crank by orthodox scientists and the U. S. Airforce called fools for encouraging him. Ball Lightning, also known as Fireballs, has been observed since prehistoric times but is a relatively new phenomenon for scientific study. A 'fireball' should not be confused with flashes of lightning which are the normal manifestations of electrical storms. It is generally described as a 'ball of fire' which falls from the sky and moves about on earth causing fires and frightening simple folk before it suddenly disappears. I even remember as a child being very frightened by a particular violent thunderstorm and afterwards being told that a fireball had been responsible for the explosion I had heard. The neighbours said that it had come out of the sky and damaged the roof of a nearby house.

Anecdotal reports of balls of fire were rejected by scientists as folk stories, old-wives tales, confused reports or even hallucinations. In short, no respectable scientist believed that such things could exist. It seems that only within the last ten years have fireballs had the sense to present themselves to 'reliable witnesses' so that they can be taken seriously.

Several well documented sightings have since occurred: a fireball which appeared inside an aircraft, Ball Lightning which ended up in a butt of water and boiled the contents dry. Meteorologists were at last forced to agree that the evidence for their existence was pretty strong. The general conclusion was that fireballs contain a great deal of energy, are stable for several minutes and appear to be electrical in origin.

Several theories were put forward to account for the phenomenon. One school of thought argued that very high temperatures could be produced in a natural electrical discharge, high enough for a nuclear reaction involving the atoms in the air to occur. Others thought that a fireball consisted of a stable electrical plasma which existed at very high temperatures. Both theories would have sounded as exotic as flying saucers in the first half of the century. I began to see why Project Tesla had the support of the U.S. Air Force. If a fireball indeed contains a very high temperature reaction which can hold itself together for several minutes, then it could contain an important clue for thermonuclear power development. Thermonuclear power, or nuclear fusion, is one of the power sources projected for the future. Fusion can generate far more energy than conventional nuclear power (fission) and its raw material is abundant – hydrogen from seawater. It is not too difficult to begin the fusing reaction but the problem is that of containing it and preventing the hot reacting gases from flying apart. Most research has been focussed on keeping the high temperature gases together for a fraction of a second using 'magnetic bottles.' But despite the money pumped into the project both in the U.S. and U.S.S.R., actual energy production lies far into the future. The problem of containment or stability was proving far too difficult. But supposing that nature had discovered a way to control such an intense reaction? I could see not only the U.S. Airforce becoming interested in fireballs, for they could be a living example of a new field of physics.

I realized that in one sense Tesla's invention had proved a great success. It enabled very high voltages to be generated, sufficient to study this new and curious phenomenon of nature. But the success of the Tesla Transmitter in generating fireballs was still a far cry from anything to do with power transmission.

After I had finished making notes on my conversation with Golka I began to read about Tesla's first years in the States and realized that I was seeing yet another facet of his character – Nikola Tesla, businessman.

Towards the end of the century Thomas Edison had cornered the market in the commercial development of electrical power. With the opening of his public power station on September 4, 1882, in New York City, the Edison system seemed destined to be installed in every American town. Edison himself had developed a power generation and supply system which was based on low voltage direct current and even in the face of Tesla's new invention he was to cling stubbornly to his original ideas.

The main problem with direct current supply at the turn of the century was that it could only be generated at low voltages. Unlike alternating current which can be stepped-up by transformer, D.C. could not be increased in voltage.

Modern transmission lines carry electrical power at high voltage for the simple reason that the higher the voltage the lower the losses due to line resistance. In the Edison system resistive losses were so high that power could only be transmitted over fairly short distances. Each city was required to have its own power station and there was little hope of electricity being taken to outlying districts or small villages.

Thomas Edison's major rival was George Westinghouse who had realized, as Tesla had done, that A.C. power could be stepped up to higher voltages by transformer and then transmitted at very low loss. In 1886 Westinghouse constructed a test transmission line in which current at 3,000 volts was carried a distance of 4,000 feet.

Edison for his part refused to move; his giant corporation was committed to D.C. power and he forged ahead building improved generators and transmission lines. He felt confident in his position, for he knew that his own system had been tried and trusted by his satisfied clients, while the Westinghouse generators were far from successful. The great American inventor was by no means the lone reactionary when it came to high voltage A.C. power, for the International Niagara Commission headed by the leading physicist of the day, Lord Kelvin, had decided in favour of direct current.

The same year that Mark Twain published *Huckleberry Finn* and Hiram Maxim invented his automatic gun, Nikola Tesla landed in New York and approached Thomas Alva Edison with the plans for his great electrical invention. Edison was not sympathetic, although he did offer the new immigrant a position in his company.

The following year Tesla was on his own again and, financed by interested businessmen, he patented a new system of street lighting in the name of 'The Tesla Electric Light and Manufacturing Company, of Rahway, New Jersey'.

To have incorporated oneself and filed such a series of patents is no mean achievement, yet it appears that by the end of the same year Tesla's funds had run out and he was forced to work as a labourer. By 1887 he had again found backers and this time used their money to construct a laboratory and workshop. For the next few weeks his energies were directed towards the vision he had been given back in Budapest in 1882. Tesla's ideas were crystallized into a series of drawings and working models of all aspects of his transmission system. By the end of the year some forty patents had been applied for. Under the agreement Tesla had made with his investors, he would retain 50 per cent of the rewards from his invention.

The following year represented the climax of Tesla's career. On May 8, 1888, the major patents were granted and a week later he lectured on high voltage power transmission to the American Association of Electrical Enginers.

A copy of this lecture reached the desk of George Westinghouse who immediately arranged a meeting with Tesla. Their encounter was to sow the seed from which our modern age would grow, for a combination of Westinghouse's corporate resources and Tesla's inventions would sweep the continent. Westinghouse offered Tesla one million dollars plus royalties for the patent rights. Tesla insisted on a royalty of one dollar per horsepower.

The two men shook hands and the War of the Currents began.

Westinghouse at once began to manufacture the various components of the Tesla system and offered his partner $2,000 per month plus one third of royalties to supervise his Pittsburgh plant. Tesla declined, for he was more interested in returning to the peace and quiet of his New York laboratory where he had begun to experiment on ultra high voltages and frequencies.

The inventor was not destined to spend long in this Ivory Tower, however, for the War of the Currents was hotting up. Edison had placed all his corporate eggs in the basket of D.C. power and now he was faced with a rival system. To make matters worse, he had once been offered the chance to buy Tesla's inventions before they had even been patented.

In the heat of battle Edison wrote, in the *North American Review* for November, 1889:

> My personal desire would be to prohibit entirely the use of alternating currents. They are as unnecessary as they are dangerous.

Edison was a showman and having the town lights switched on by Thomas A. Edison was an event to remember. The town of Anaheim, California for example, celebrated its new Edison system with concerts, marches and displays. The 'Grand Talking Machine.' 'Edison Moving Picture Machine' and Minescope featuring Dr. Eugene Sandow 'The Modern Hercules' were displayed. The current itself was turned on by Mr. Charles Lorenz, the 'oldest living resident' of Anaheim and the magical day was celebrated by a concert involving recitations and 'whistling solos.'

Edison must have realized that whistling solos alone would not be sufficient to win the day against a superior system, so he looked around for another point of attack. It was provided when, ironically, the Edison Company installed, under licence, an electric chair in Auburn State Prison in 1890. The world's first all electric execution proved a messy affair. It did not go unnoticed by the press that 'Tesla current' was used. The inference was obvious, if A.C. can be used to dispatch dangerous criminals, is it really the thing to have about the home? AC power is hazardous, Edison had said, and far too lethal to bring amongst the women and children.

An attack which focussed on the safety of Westinghouse's system was a master stroke, for it totally ignored economic and scientific arguments, on which score Edison was bound to lose. How could Westinghouse reply to the accusation that he was endangering the safety of American homes? His position seems not unlike that of the directrs of nuclear power associations today who must deal with charges of radiation hazards and possible nuclear accidents. No matter what they say, they are lost, for the public is suspicious of any attempt to deal with the issues which remotely looks like a 'cover-up' or a minimization of risk. Even if safety arguments look good on paper, can an individual afford to take the risk?

Tesla's counterblast in the 'War of the Currents' was even more brilliant than Edison's attack. He made no attempt to answer the arguments or present an analysis of the risks involved. Instead he walked out of his laboratory and on to the stage. Nikola Tesla became a bigger showman than Edison. In lecture halls and exhibitions, Tesla assembled his electrical apparatus and barnstormed for AC current. His displays must have been spectacular, even by today's standards. He produced enormous flashes of lightning across the stage, he activated machines which flashed and cracked and, at the high point of his act, allowed high voltage electrical current to pass through his body and light a row of electric lamps.

From his earliest days Tesla had been inspired by the vision of harnessing nature's powers - waterfalls, rivers and winds. With the Edison system, a waterfall powered generating station was quite possible but there would have been enormous losses in transmitting the current to nearby towns. With Tesla's high voltage A.C. generation, the power could be transported across the continent if necessary. His vision, when it came to electrical power, was unlimited and he was determined to win the War of the Currents against Thomas Edison.

Tesla's displays won the day, for by demonstrating the power and excitement of electricity with himself a human conductor, he had thrown fear out of the window. In 1893, the World Columbian Exposition in Chicago was lit by the Tesla system and in 1896, hydroelectric power was carried from Niagara Falls to the city of Buffalo.

Today the electrical power lines which supply North America and the rest of the world are direct descendants of the system Tesla patented at the end of the last century. Tesla's electrical motors are to be found in every factory, and A.C. induction generators are now powered by everything from coal to atomic energy.

The War of the Currents added another dimension to my picture of Nikola Tesla. Not only was he an inspired inventor and a dedicated scientist but he had turned out to be a shrewd businessman who had been able to drive a good bargain. In addition, he had a gift which is unusual in most scientists, showmanship, and the ability to explain his inventions and researches to the general public.

Yet what began as a clever and useful way of introducing AC current to the general public ended up as an obsessive need for publicity. Towards the end of his life Tesla bombarded the offices of the leading newspapers with reports of his latest astounding invention. In some cases the editors did not always know what to make of these announcements, particularly when they involved communications with other planets.

I wondered what an editor in the early years of the century would have made of one of the following excerpts:

> My measurements and calculations have shown that it is perfectly practicable to produce on our globe, by the use of these principles, an electrical movement of such magnitude that, without the slightest doubt, its effect will be perceptible on some of our nearer planets, as Venus and Mars. Thus from mere possibility interplanetary communication has entered the stage of probability.... hat we can send a message to a planet is certain,

that we can get an answer is probable; man is not the only being in the Infinite gifted with mind.

High-frequency currents especially have a great future. The time will come when this form of electrical energy will be available in every private residence. I consider it quite possible that through their surface actions we may do away with the customary bath.... Such a dry bath, besides being convenient and time-saving, would also be of beneficial therapeutic influence.

We have soon to have everywhere smoke annihilators, dust absorbers, ozonizers, sterilizers of water, air, food and clothing, and accident preventers on streets, elevated roads and in subways. It was become next to impossible to contact disease germs or get hurt in the city, and country folk will go to town to rest and get better.

Tesla was not only ahead of his time, he was ahead of ours!

Chapter Ten

EARLY THE FOLLOWING week, I was on a morning flight from Ottawa to Toronto. As I reclined in my seat after take-off, I began to review my thoughts about Nikola Tesla yet again. In a couple of hours I would be speaking to the electrical engineer who had helped Tim Richardson in the planning stages of his Tesla Transmitter. From my conversation with Golka, it appeared that the Tower actually produced the high voltages Tesla claimed. But did this imply that the Tower could also transmit energy? As far as I could see Broadcast Power was as much a problem as it had ever been. Energy dissipation was the main objection and the idea of containment by charged layers in the upper atmosphere did not seem promising.

My thoughts were interrupted by a voice telling me that we would soon be landing at Toronto Airport. Forty minutes later, after the business of finding a cab, I was outside the Department of Electrical Engineering of the University of Toronto. I walked up the main steps and saw Janischewski's name listed with other staff members on a board inside the entrance. When I reached his office I found him engaged in a telephone discussion with a colleague in California. As I sat down to wait I noticed his degrees and awards which were framed on the wall. Janischewski appeared to be a man with a respected reputation in the scientific community.

At last the phone call came to an end and he stood up and apologized for the dealy.

'It's Dr. Peat for the N.R.C, isn't it?'

'Yes,' I replied. 'I'm looking into some proposals made by a man called Nikola Tesla and I was wondering if you would be able to help me?'

Janischewski smiled. 'I'll try too You see I've read some of Tesla's papers and I've found them all very interesting. He was so much ahead of his time.'

I nodded and asked him, 'Could you tell me how you first got interested in Tesla?'

'Some time ago a young man called Tim Richardson came to see me. He was building a device based on one of Tesla's patents and he was having a few problems. He wanted to discuss it with me. That's how I began to look at the patents.'

'What was your reaction?' I asked.

'Well, as I said, they're interesting. I'm not really an expert on Tesla, I haven't the time, but I do think that there's something worthwhile in all this.'

'You mean, you think Power Transmission is possible?'

'Oh, I don't know about that,' Janischewski answered. 'I'm talking about the device itself. It's a very, very clever design. If you looked at it quickly you'd probably say that it could never work. I don't think that many engineers could sit down today and design a 20 million volt transformer.'

I took a pen and some paper from my brief case and began to take notes.

'What is so special about Tesla's design?' I asked.

'Well let's say that a normal transformer would simply break down if you tried to operate it at such a high voltage. Sparks would begin to break out between the coils, the insulation would disintegrate, the whole thing just couldn't work at really high voltages. You see the voltage differences between each of the turns in the coil would be so high that the transformer would just keep discharging.'

'How did Tesla get over that?' I asked.

'He used an extremely clever design. Tesla took account of everything, the shape and geometry of the coil, the thickness of the wire, the exact space between each loop of the coil. He was able to distribute the high voltage swings exactly how he wanted them. He arranged so that the biggest swing in the voltage would occur right at the top of the coil and not between the wires in the coil. Do you remember that in one of his designs he had a ball on top of the tower? Well, the whole thing makes use of resonance effects so that the biggest voltage swings occur right on the ball and he completely avoids discharges and insulation breakdown.'

'So this means that Tesla's design would have to be followed exactly,' I added.

'Yes, that's what Tim Richardson found. I don't think the Transmitter would work otherwise. But let me give you an example from my own work. You see when lightning strikes a power line you get a surge of high voltage and this runs along the transmission line until it hits a transformer or a circuit breaker. Now when a high voltage surge reaches a transformer the result is a blow-out. You get a power failure followed by expensive repairs. Of course, electrical enginers build safety devices but people have also tried to design transformers which could withstand a sudden surge without breaking down altogether. The idea is to design the geometry of the coils in the transformer so that the biggest swings in voltage occur only in the outer layer. The design is pretty complicated and the whole thing has to be done on a computer. There are a lot of equations to be solved.'

'I see; does the whole thing work?'

'Yes. If you get the distance between the coils right and your geometry correct, then such a transformer can stand up to a power surge. But this was exactly what Tesla did in the 1890's. He built a transformer which actually resonated under a continuous power surge and he didn't even have a computer to help him.'

I nodded in reply and added, 'People say that he saw the designs directly in his imagination.'

Janischewski continued, 'It would be very interesting to study one of these towers. We could learn a great deal about high voltages and about the relationship between high voltage and high frequency current. I think that the results would be very useful.'

I looked up from my writing and asked him another question. 'I don't like to put you on the spot, but do you think that the tower could be used for power transmission?'

'As I said I'm not an expert.' Janischewski thought for a moment. 'I don't think I believe any of these explanations of power transmission I've read.'

I smiled, 'So you don't think that there's much in it?'

'No not really. But .... well, there is just one thing. Do you remember Tesla's experiments with worldwide communication?'

'Yes, he was trying to broadcast from Long Island. I guess that Marconi beat him to it.'

Janischewski smiled. 'I think that it would have been very interesting if Tesla had got there first. You see his method was different from Marconi's. Both of them knew that radio waves were produced by an oscillating electric current and that you could send messages by modulating the oscillations. What Marconi did was to build an electronic circuit which oscillated and then he fed that oscillating current into an antenna. The current in the antenna is the thing responsible for sendng out the radio waves but in Marconi's case the total process isn't all that efficient. In Tesla's design he set the whole tower in resonance. His tower acted both as oscillator and antenna at the same time. I think that the process may have been far more efficient and Tesla was able to handle a great deal of power.'

I did not have time to discuss this idea with Dr. Janischewski for his telephone had begun to ring again and he was soon engaged in a new conversation. I signalled my thanks and left his office.

I spent the next few days in Toronto visiting the bookstores and record shops. Since I was in the city I took the opportunity of contacting a few of the scientists who I had been told were experts on the weather. As I had expected, I found them to be dubious about Microwski's claim that the weather was being modified. They agreed that small changes in rainfall, fog dispersion and the like were possible over local areas but it had not been possible to modify weather on a global scale.

I pointed out that the method was supposed to be radically new but they countered this by telling me that no major changes had been observed in the weather over the last few years. It seemed to me that weather modification was another of those claims which seemed impossible to substantiate. No respectable meteorologist felt that the weather was being altered. On the other hand, there was a general agreement that weather mechanics was not yet well understood.

Back in Ottawa again I talked to other scientists about Tesla Power Transmission, for I felt it necessary to check my own objectivity and make sure I had left no electrical stone unturned. The reaction was unanimous; even if the Tesla Magnifying Transmitter could generate the high voltages its inventor claimed, the device could never broadcast power with even the crudest efficiency.

One electrical engineer I met produced figures based on the United States 'Project Sanguine' (broadcasting very low frequency signals to submarines). Even with the gigantic antenna the project required, its efficiency would be quite low. His figures seemed persuasive yet I was reminded of Tesla's claim that his own system of broadcasting differed from Marconi's and Janischewski's remark that, when it came to radio, a Tesla Magnifying Transmitter may be far more efficient than a conventional system.

When it came to Tesla's claim that his transmitted signals returned with increased strength and that he had tapped into an inexhaustible source of power my colleagues gave me amused looks of derision. I had to agree, the problem with 'Cosmic Power' was that I had no clear idea of what this 'inexhaustible source' represented. Nowhere in his writings, as far as I could discover, did Tesla take the time to spell out how this power operated or where it came from. Was it the voltage generated between the earth and upper atmosphere, I wondered? Did it originate in outer space? Tesla was being his usual elusive self.

One important document remained to be studied. The theory proposed by Andrija Puharich to account for Tesla's Transmission. Possibly this paper would supply the clues I had been seeking.

As I read 'The Physics of the Tesla Magnifying Transmitter and the Transmission of Electrical Power Without Wires', I realized that Puharich had pulled out all his scientific stops. He argued that the secret of Tesla power transmission lay in the very high voltages which were generated in the coil. He wrote of 'Advanced Signals,' 'de Broglie's phase waves' and through their invocation devised a theory for guided power transmission.

In essence Puharich argued that the transmitter operated with two different kinds of electromagnetic radiation, 'Retarded Potentials' and 'Advanced Potentials'. The 'Retarded', as he correctly pointed out, is associated with conventional broadcasting and consists of electromagnetic waves spreading out from the transmitter at the speed of light.

As to the 'Advanced' radiation, Puharich claimed that this form of electromagnetic signal had been ignored by orthodox science. It was supposed to stream out from the transmitter at speeds greater than that of light and form a link with the receiver. This link took the form of a rotating magnetic field or 'wormhole' which burrowed through the earth. According to this theory the Advanced Signals were not actually responsible for transmitting power but established the magnetic tunnel through which energy then flowed.

Puharich next argued that the very high electrical fields generated in the Tesla Tower would produce elementary particles (electron-positron pairs) which then moved through the wormhole carrying electrical energy.

The obvious advantage of the theory was that a source of Cosmic Power had been suggested. This was the 'vacuum state', that hypothetical reservoir of infinite energy posited by elementary particle scientists. According to Puharich the high voltages of the Tesla Magnifying Transmitter created electron-positron pairs out of this vacuum state and released a considerable amount of energy at the same time. It was a theoretical case of getting something for nothing.

At voltages in excess of 100,000,000, resonating oscillations would excite the vacuum state and cause a stream of elementary particles to flow along magnetic wormholes which tunnelled their way through the earth.

Where Tesla had been vague Puharich has been specific and I gave him credit for an ingenious theory. He had understood the objections to Tesla Transmission and attempted to answer

them all within a single theory. There was only one problem – the theory was very obviously wrong.

To begin with, Advanced Signals were not the mysterious
and neglected forms of radiation Puharich claimed they were.
Back in the nineteenth century the Scottish physicist James
Clerk Maxwell had worked out the equations which govern all
electromagnetic phenomena, from light to gamma rays and
from radio to X-rays. Each solution to this set of equations,
called Retarded Solutions, represents some physically possible
state of affairs in the world of radiation. A radio signal
spreading out from a transmitter, for example, or the beam of a
searchlight.

There was, however, one curiousity about Maxwell's Equations. And this is a curiousity which occurs in many of the
other fundamental equations of physics as well. To each
solution, or physical situation, there corresponded its twin or
mirror image. These mirror image solutions were called the
Advanced Solutions and take the form of electromagnetic
waves moving backwards in time. In a sense the Advanced
Solutions were the light waves and radio broadcasts of some
parallel universe in which clocks run in reverse.

Puharich had totally misunderstood the nature of Advanced
Solutions by thinking that they travelled 'faster than light' and
took the form of magnetic wormholes. In simple terms these
hypothetical signals would violate causality if they ever existed
in nature. We would see the light from a distant searchlight
before the beam had been switched on. An astronaut communicating by Advanced Signals would hear the voice of mission
control before the controller had begun to speak. Such signals
could only exist in a world in which time ran backwards.

Far from being neglected, as Puharich suggested, Advanced
Signals had been well studied. The brilliant physicist, Richard
Feynmann, had tried to use the solutions in one of his earliest
theories. When looking at the problem of radiation and
thermodynamics in a Black Hole, I had once posed the
possibility of Advanced Signals being able to escape from its
centre.

As to wormholes through the ground, well this was pure

nonsense as well. The idea, I knew, came from some work by the imaginative American physicist, John Wheeler, who had once suggested that submicroscopic 'wormholes' which existed in a fifth dimension could interconnect parts of the universe.

Although I knew that Puharich's theory contained several errors and misunderstandings I was certainly enjoying it. The ideas were crazy but so were Quarks and Tachyons, White Holes and Multiple Universes, and all the other far out toys that respectable physicists had invented to play with. Puharich's inexhaustible source of energy was 'the vacuum state' out of which pairs of elementary particles were supposed to be created. His actual argument was a little faulty here but the outlandish idea of a vacuum which contains an infinite amount of energy is cherished by a great many theoretical physicists and it amounts to sacrilege to doubt its existence.

Chapter Eleven

As I PUT aside this paper by Andrija Puharich I realized that I had come to the end of the Tesla file. I had read and studied its contents and tried to follow each of the leads it offered. Over the past weeks I had spoken to people who knew something about the Tesla Magnifying Transmitter and I now knew that it was an ingenious instrument capable of operating at very high power and at unheard of voltages.

No one, however, outside the members of P.A.C.E., had been able to hold out any hope for power transmissions. The only evidence that the whole process wasn't just science fiction came from Tesla's rather vague notebooks and as far as I knew the only other living witness was Dr. Arthur Matthews whom I had been unable to locate.

What was there in the way of circumstantial evidence? The most pressing argument was from the suggestion that Russian scientists had built a Tesla Transmitter and were at present using it to change the world's weather. Now there were certainly some secret transmission experiments being carried out in Russia but it did not follow that they had anything to do with Nikola Tesla. As far as weather modification went, I could obtain no evidence except the claim made by Andrew Microwski.

Now the time had come to collect my notes together and write a report. I was quite sure tht given an indefinite amount of time I would be able to gather more facts – I could, for example, wait until Tim Richardson had built and tested his Tesla Tower. I could locate and question Arthur Matthews and see if there was evidence of Transmission experiments in Quebec. But I felt I had enough to go on.

I allowed my thoughts on Tesla to form into a logical shape

and began to sketch out the main ideas of my report. This process went much faster than I had anticipated and within a few days I found myself well into my first draft.

As I began to surface into the calmer waters of revisions and rewrites, I took time to read the telephone messages and letters which I had allowed to accumulate. One of them gave me a burst of pleasure as I read it. It was from an old friend of mine, David Schrum, and said that he would be dropping in to see me the following week-end.

Several years ago Dave had been a research student of mine and we had shared an office in a large room at the National Research Council. Our time together had been stimulating and profitable. We shared a vision of the goals of physics, but our approaches and personalities differed so that the discussions were challenging and tiring. Every so often we would begin a casual conversation at the blackboard only to have it blossom into a full scale voyage of discovery often carried out at the tops of our voices until we found ourselves in the dark, deserted building several hours later. We would laugh and step out into the night full of good humour and with every intention of taking up the battle again on the following day.

A year or two later we met in London while I was on my sabbatical and Dave was on a fellowship. Over pints of Guinness in pubs close to the college, or in the staff common room, our dialogue continued as before. It took us from physics to the nature of perception, from art to archetypes, and from music to religion until I would glance at my watch and run down Tottenham Court Road to catch my last train home.

On his return from England Dave felt the need to examine the roots of his scientific motivation so he rejected any chance of an academic position by retiring to a cottage some miles outside a small village in Ontario. During that period I heard little from him beyond an occasional letter or phone call. At times he mentioned a book he was working on and, at others, hinted at ongoing games of poker with the locals, nights spent reading scientific papers from the turn of the century or long walks in the country.

A year or two later he moved to the mining town of Sudbury, Ontario, and renounced his isolated life for teaching at a local college. We continued a sporadic exchange of letters and from time to time he would visit me in Ottawa. During these trips, he would explain to me that his interest in a scientific account of the universe was still as deep but he now felt that the thinker himself – the creator of science – had been left out of the picture. He concluded that an investigation of nature should not only relate to the Observed phenomena but also to the Observer, the scientist and his perceptions, consciousness and the relationship between his thought and the language he uses. These goals, Dave felt, had to be approached in an oblique and patient way, there was no need to rush things or write down his thoughts in the form of a book or scientific paper.

I looked forward to the arrival of my friend and spent the intervening time polishing my report on Tesla Power Transmission. Early on Friday afternoon I left my office and headed home.

The day had moved into late afternoon when I heard someone at the front door. Dave Schrum stood on the doorstep, a zippered bag in one hand and a collection of brown paper bags in the other.

'It looked like a nice day so I walked from the bus.' He pushed past me into the hall. 'Do you mind if I put these in the kitchen?'

'These' proved to be the collection of brown paper bags containing nuts, lentils and chick peas. My friend looked down at me as if to gauge my reaction. 'I've become more interested in the textures of food than in flavours and smells. If you don't mind I'll get started and cook for myself.'

I laughed and made some remark about his vital bodily fluids not being able to survive on such a diet and sat down to watch. As Dave busied himself with the preparation of his evening meal, we began to chat.

Once Dave had transferred his magical mixture from the pan to his plate I said:

'There's something I'd like to talk to you about, Dave,' and handed him some papers. 'It's taken up most of my time for the past few weeks.'

David glanced at the papers for a moment then set them down beside his plate. 'I'll look at them later,' he said.

After his meal Dave asked if he could go up to his bedroom and lie down. 'I'll take this stuff with me and try to read it.'

I went back into the living room, selected Bach's Brandenburg Concertos and began to wait. In several hours I assumed that Dave must have gone to sleep so I made my own way upstairs, but his door opened and he poked his head out.

'I think I'd better go for a walk. Could you tell me the best way?'

I gave him some general directions, then headed for my own bedroom. As I was getting into bed, I heard the front door slam but I was long asleep before Dave returned.

The next morning when I came down to breakfast, Dave was already up and dressed with my papers collected around him on the kitchen table. He looked up at me as I entered and smiled, 'Well?' he asked.

I hesitated for a little then asked him, 'What do you think of it all?'

Dave looked at me. 'It's good. I like what you've written very much. It's clear. I think it must have been a terrible mess to sort out.'

I enjoyed his compliment but wanted to press on. 'Yes, but what do you really think of it?'

Dave smiled a little self-consciously. 'At the beginning when I read about what Tesla wanted to do I really hoped that it would work.... I know that sounds silly. But then as I read through your notes I had to agree with you – it would be really interesting to build one of these things but you can't use it to transmit power.'

I felt relieved. Dave was the first person who had seen my draft report and its conclusions. I also knew him to be a stern critic who would be able to spot any loopholes or sloppy arguments.

'Well that's that,' I said. 'But I know what you meant when you said that you wished Tesla had been right. He was such a strange man ... all that vision. Do you know how he got hold of his ideas?'

I began to explain all that I had read about Tesla and the

curious fashion in which pictures would appear in his imagination. Dave listened with great concentration as I sketched out the story of Nikola Tesla and his hopes and plans for the future. As I drew near to giving some sort of conclusion about Tesla and his life Dave suddenly stood up and said, 'Let's go to the waterfall'.

The waterfall had once been a curious symbol for us both. It had been a meeting place and a focus for our thoughts. The falls themselves were modest when compared with something as powerful as Tesla's Niagara, but they had a character and a temperment all their own. We had visited the falls in winter and summer and had studied their moods.

The falls represented the meeting point of the Rideau and Ottawa rivers and were located very close to the building which had housed the office we had shared. In the winter, we would walk briskly to the falls after lunch and remark upon the complex patterns of ice left by the spray. In summer we could spend an hour or more looking down into the water and watching its movements. We used to joke that all the secrets of nature were contained within that waterfall. If we could only grasp the meaning of its eddies and currents, if we could describe the patterns of its flowing, then we would have discovered a clue to the central mystery of the universe.

Now, several years later, we looked down into the same waters and were no closer to understanding them. Dave broke a stick and allowed small pieces of wood to fall into the river below. He watched intently as they were gathered up by the water and flung far down into the boiling confusion of the falls.

'It's funny about Tesla, isn't it?' he asked eventually.

I nodded and he had no need to look up at me.

'There was something about his obsession,' he went on, 'I think that it even got to you in the end. That picture of the future and all the power and confidence of his writing. I think that's why he's attracted so many people.'

We were silent for a little as we watched the segments of wood drop into the water. Some were swept away in seconds, others became trapped in an eddy for several minutes until they too joined the fast flowing river. 'But look how he ended up, a recluse just walking the streets,' I said. 'He spent his whole future. He patented hundreds of inventions but look how he ended.'

Dave stopped working at this stick and looked at me directly: 'I believe that it's not too difficult to let yourself get obsessed by something. You get eaten up by it and spend your whole life pitting yourself against something ... it becomes the only meaning to existence. I don't think most people even realize that it's happened, they keep going until they drop.'

The conversation seemed to be taking a depressing turn so we began to walk. I recalled that many times in the past Dave's analysis of hopes and ambitions had suddenly taken on an atmosphere of sadness. This time I found myself trapped in this sadness as well.

'You know I had some intimation about all this when I first read his life story,' I explained. 'It talked about him dedicating his life to science - he wanted to embrace pure reason for the good of the human race and he was determined to cut out the emotional side of his nature. At the time I had the feeling that it would lead to his destruction.'

We walked in silence then Dave faced me again, 'Was it all a metaphor - this business of power towers which could link the earth?'

I understood at once what he meant, in fact it had been on my mind for the past few days but I hadn't wanted to bring it to consciousness.

'Yes, I think so,' I nodded. 'It all comes back to Jung again doesn't it?'

We both laughed and I began to tell Dave how I felt about it all.

'You see Tesla was always talking about linking the world with energy. His whole life was obsessed with electrical power - with motors, generators, transmitting power. Think what it must have been like, seventy, eighty years ago. Electricity was a mysterious and dangerous power, you couldn't hold it or see it. It came out of the very heart of nature. But Tesla spent every waking hour wrestling with this dark force; he had to tame it. Remember how he even passed high voltages through his body. Then in the end he speaks of finding an inexhaustible source of the power from within the earth.'

Dave nodded to encourage me, 'Yes, you're getting there. It's all making sense.'

I went on, 'The next thing he does is build these towers, he wants to stretch out this power. He wants to reach across the continent, right across the globe. He's going to link the whole world with this force. Everything will be crossed by this network of power and look what sort of a a world it's going to be.... peace and harmony, no more war, no more want, no friction because there is enough power to do anything the world wants. It's a sort of universal brotherhood brought about by this dark force of nature which Tesla had tamed.'

We had both stopped on the path and I realized that we were becoming quite animated. Dave reached out with his hands and asked, 'And this force? What was it really?'

'Yes, that's it. What did he cut from his own nature as a young man – love, friendship, sorrow, hatred, hope and fear? He thought that if he could throw away everything that was emotional and confusing and disturbing to his logical mind then he would achieve greatness.'

We began to walk on together. 'You know when he got older he became a complete recluse – he even developed a phobia about germs. He was supposed to ask for a whole set of napkins when he went out to eat and then he'd carefully polish each dish and then his knife and fork, he went as far as throwing away his gloves as soon as he'd worn them. He hated touching people.'

'Yes, you must be right,' Dave said. 'He thought that he'd rid himself of his feelings but he spent the rest of his life trying to tame them. It was all a metaphor – that tower. Feeling, love, friendship, reaching out to the rest of the world. He called it electrical power, transmission directly without wires, a world linked to a source of inexhaustible energy, a brotherhood in the futre, the new Golden Age. That's what must have carried him on all along.'

I agreed, 'I think that you're right. And people must pick up feeling from his writings. After all it's a good message, a world linked by love; I think that's why all this Tesla stuff is so attractive to them.'

I suddenly began to laugh and Dave looked at me in a puzzled way. 'What is it?' he asked.

'Oh, I just thought, if anyone could hear us they would think we were mad. Think of it: I'm supposed to produce a scientific report for the government on power transmission and I end up talking about love.'

Dave joined in my laughter, 'Yes, you'd better keep quiet about it. After all, they don't know the great secret - they're all even crazier than we are!'

Chapter Twelve

I WAS SITTING in the President's office again. This time the day seemed brighter and the sun shone with more force, although so little time seemed to have passed since my first visit.

I had placed a copy of my report on the table and Dr. Schneider was now turning its pages in silence. After some time he looked up at me: 'Thank you, it's very clear.'

He gathered the papers together again, tapped them on his desk and placed them back in their folder, the matter seemed closed to him.

'So you don't think it'll work?'

'No.'

Schneider looked down at this desk, then smiled: 'You don't seem to think much of the theoretical explanation these people put together, Puharich wasn't it?'

'I'm quite certain it's wrong,' I said.

There were a few moments silence between us, then I began again, 'But I'm still interested in the transmitter as a matter of fact. Tim Richardson is trying to build something along the lines of one of Tesla's patents.'

I tried to catch Schneider's attention with this remark but he did not look up. Instead he reached for the file and began to search through my report absentmindedly.

'Tesla was quite ahead of his time,' he said. 'I suppose you've read some of the biographies? I think you can see how he was led to this idea of power transmission by this interest in resonance and then his experiments with conduction in gases.'

I tried again, 'If Richardson gets a Tesla tower built it may be worth taking a look at it. It could be interesting.'

Schneider nodded, 'Richardson sounds like a responsible

young man. I'd certainly like to look over his results when he begins his experiments.'

I posed a question with my eyes and Schneider continued to speak.

'But we have so many projects of our own – I don't see how we can help. The whole thing should be properly documented of course. There's been far too much vagueness about the whole thing ... no proper records.'

I nodded and shut my briefcase, 'Well that's it, I suppose. If anything else turns up I'll let you know.'

'Thank you. And I do think you've done a good job', he paused for a moment, 'This report will be sent to the Prime Minister so I'll have to send a letter with it. Let me have some sort of a draft – list the main points of the report so that I can draw his attention to them.'

I agreed.

'There's just one more thing. Nothing is secret about all this but it would be good manners not to distribute the report at the moment. It wouldn't be a good idea if too many people had access to it before the P.M. has a chance to read it himself. After that ... well, we could write something for one of the scientific journals and publish it as an article.'

I said that it sounded like a good idea and walked to the door.

Back in my office, I began spring cleaning. I gathered together all my Tesla notes, clippings, articles and correspondence, and stuffed them into a couple of big boxes. Next I piled up the reference books I had been using and, with a clean desk, I began the task of going through all those unanswered messages I had allowed to accumulate over the last few months.

For the first few days things seemed empty. I had spent so much time and concentration on Nikola Tesla and now it was over. I had a feeling that within a few weeks the whole business would be dead and buried so I was now faced with the problem of focussing on some new activity.

I was not so naive as to think that my report would discourage the members of P.A.C.E. They seemed so firm in their conviction and support for Tesla's plans that after reading my objections, they would soon bounce back to optimism. On the other hand, I had the feeling that once word of this report had got around, other scientists would proceed with greater caution when approached by Tesla enthusiasts. I realized that I was a little sad. Tesla had been condemned to obscurity so many years ago, in the past couple of years he had experienced a temporary burst of publicity but the was again sentenced to be placed on the dusty shelves of some library bookstack.

I was wrong: a week or so later Tesla was back in the newspapers again. A story was circulating that Russian transmitters were being used to modify the earth's weather. It was said that the West would soon experience devastating storms and changes of climate. In the midst of all this, the telephone started to ring: 'Was I the same Dr. David Peat who was engaged in scientific research on Tesla Transmitters?' 'Was it true that the Canadian Government was about to finance Tesla Research?' 'Had I published a secret report on Tesla Transmission?'

I realized very quickly that my report was not as confidential as I had thought. Within a couple of days, televisions and radio stations were planning items and reports on Tesla Transmission and CBC radio was working on an hour long documentary. I realized that the best thing to do would be to come straight out into the open and agree to give interviews and every help to the reporters.

Over the following weeks news of weather modification was fuelled by stories of the Tesla Transmitter or a new source of energy. The story peaked and a handful of days later had faded from view. It was during this decline in the popularity of the Tesla story that I received a call from Andrew Microwski. Would I join him and Senator Carter of Newfoundland for lunch at the Parliament Buildings.

I approached that lunch with some misgivings. I did not imagine that the Senator and his friends would be very happy with my report and I realized that I was in for a rather hard time. By some 'Freudian' process, I was late for our meeting but as I arrived at the member's dining room, I recognised Andrew talking to two other people at the entrance.

Andrew introduced me to the elderly white haired gentleman who turned out to be Senator Carter. As we made our way to a table the Senator asked me a few questions about my background. Where had I trained? How long had I been in Canada? Did I enjoy living in Ottawa?

As we began our meal, the Senator suggested that I should give him a brief summary of my reaction to Tesla's proposals. I began to speak and he listened in silence until, towards the end of my explanation, he asked me if I had actually read any of Tesla's patents.

I decided to turn the tables a little so I asked Senator Carter how he had first become interested in Tesla's work. The Senator explained that he came from one of the economically poorest areas of Canada - the province of Newfoundland - and had always wanted to do something to improve his place of birth. At university he studied science but had a growing feeling that he should go into politics. This vocation had been a success for he had risen to the position of Canadian Senator. But he still retained his early dream to do something to improve his province and this was why he had first become interested in Tesla Power Transmission.

In addition to the massive island in the Gulf of the St. Lawrence River, Newfoundland province includes the barren and sparsely populated sea coast of Labrador on the Canadian mainland. With the building of a large hydro-electric project Labrador had suddenly become an energy-rich region producing power which was badly needed by the rest of the province. The only problem was that geographically this power had to pass through the province of Quebec before it could be fed across the Straits of Belle Isle to the island of Newfoundland. Since power was essentially being sold from Labrador to Quebec and then back to Newfoundland again, the province found itself in the ironic position of paying a stranger for its own energy. The Senator hoped that Tesla Transmission could be used to transport power direct from the hydro-electric generating station to Newfoundland homes and industry without the need for transmission lines across the province of Quebec.

I could appreciate the sense of the scheme but reflected on the gulf between scientist and politician. To the scientist Broadcast Power was a revolutionary and world-shattering concept; by contrast, the politician was forced to think in terms of limited and realizable goals. Politically the merit of a scheme lies in the real possibility of its achievement rather than in abstract paper dreams. Yet I couldn't help being both shocked and amused that Tesla's grandiose vision of the future of the world should have been reduced to inter-provincial politics.

I came back to earth and suggested that my conclusions were that Broadcast Power did not look like a very efficient way of transmitting energy. Andrew Microwski interrupted me:

'I'm afraid that Dr. Puharich has made several objections to your report. He feels that you have misinterpreted some of the equations in his paper.'

I shrugged my shoulders and smiled. 'I think it's the other way about. Puharich hasn't understood his own equations. Still if he thinks I'm wrong then I'd be happy to discuss it with him.'

'Would you be willing to meet Puharich and go over the paper with him?' Andrew asked.

'Sure. Just arrange a time and give me a call. I think it's very important that everything should be done out in the open. If he believes I've made a mistake and he can show me, then I'll be willing to apologise – in print if you like.'

With our coffee we began to chat about other topics. I realized that neither Andrew nor the Senator had tried to argue with me or dispute my conclusions. One of us brought up the topic of Russian experiments and Andrew began to hint at more sinister possibilities – control of behaviour and interference with the human brain. At the time I was not sure where all this came from but later I was to piece it together into some sort of pattern.

After our meal, the Senator invited me to his rooms for another talk. We strolled along the corridors to his comfortable office with its books lining the walls and heaped in piles on the floor. Carter went over to a cabinet, looked throught it for some moments and then found a paper which he handed to me.

'Tesla actually transmitted power in Canada. Arthur Matthews was with him.'

I examined the paper he had given me: it was a map of a portion of Quebec and lines were drawn across it linking several locations.

'Matthews is an old man now but if you were to look in the bush you'd probably find some of the apparatus.'

I handed the paper back:

'Look, I can't say that it's impossible or that it can never work. All I can tell you is that the explanations and theories which Tesla and Puharich or anyone else has put forward, don't hold water. I've tried to be open and honest in this investigation, I've tried to follow all the leads but I can't go any further than that. I've no reason to think that Power Transmission could ever work.'

The Senator sat back in his chair and watched me. I continued, 'You could talk about some new principle that's unknown to science. I really don't know anything about that. All I can do is judge the evidence I've been given and I can find nothing to support this idea of power transmission I think that any other scientist would agree with me.'

Senator Carter was silent as he studied my face, then he smiled and said, 'Yes, you've been very fair.'

I warmed to him, he seemed an honest and open man with a great deal of kindness in his face. I decided to go a little further.

'All these stories of Russian experiments, first it's weather modification and now its mind control: I think that harms your case. You certainly believe that Tesla was right and I don't think I can persuade you otherwise but these stories destroy your credibility. Scientists are going to be frightened off by them. I really believe that the only way you can make a good case is by presenting some hard experimental facts; keep proper records of experiments, there should be laboratory notebooks correctly kept. Give the scientists and engineers something to go on first – all these theories about wormholes and particle creation simply get in the way.'

'Well this man Richardson is building a transmitter at Timmins, we'll just have to wait and see how it turns out,' the Senator said.

'I hope that there are no hard feelings,' I added.

'No, you were just doing your job.'

For the remainder of the time we chatted about other things. I told him of my interest in the foundations of Relativity Theory and Quantum Mechanics and we speculated on the immense gravitational sources of power which may lie untapped in the universe.

Chapter Thirteen

DURING THE FOLLOWING weeks I heard little about Nikola Tesla and my interests turned to other matters. Dave Schrum called me from Sudbury but I had nothing to tell him.

One thing could not rest at the back of my mind and that was the way in which Tesla's life had changed from the success of the Niagara Falls Power Project to the recluse of later life. For, from that point, Tesla's life should have grown from strength to strength. The 1890's began well, for the inventor took lecture tours in Europe and the United States where he was honoured by many learned societies. At the same time, Tesla was thinking about the new field of high frequency currents and much of his time was spent in his New York laboratory. His latest experiments led him to speculate about radio transmissions, automated control and, fifty years before the development of the fluorescent lamp, Tesla had built phosphor-coated globes for lighting.

His interest in the phenomena of resonance continued and he built a large mechanical vibrator to study the effects of oscillations on various structures. This experiment proved so effective that Tesla was able to set up mechanical resonances in nearby buildings. His experiments were stopped by the police before the whole street collapsed!

When it came to high frequency current, Tesla was as inventive as ever. He first designed a series of alternators which could generate current at 33,000 cycles then, reaching the limit of this approach, he began to develop the Tesla Coil.

But this Ivory Tower of research did not protect its inhabitant for long. On returning from a European lecture tour Tesla discovered that the Westinghouse operation was in severe financial difficulties. Orders continued to flood in but the corporation itself was undercapitalized and verging on bankruptcy. Tesla's reaction was immediate, he was grateful to Westinghouse, the man who had first recognized the value of his invention, and he decided to sacrifice his major source of income by waiving the royalty clause of his contract.

Not many people would have agreed to forfeit a fortune, particularly when their own finances were critical. The capital sum Tesla had received from the sale of his patents had long been spent, in returns to his first backers and in the cost of building his laboratory. When, in 1895, this uninsured laboratory burned to the ground he was forced to look for private financing. John Jacob Astor and later J. P. Morgan came to his aid but this assistance was unfortunately short lived.

Tesla moved to Colorado Springs where, in 1889, he began his great series of experiments on the electrical resonances of the earth. A year later he won a moral victory as the Edison corporation converted its production line to the Tesla system.

The twentieth century found Tesla at Long Island in his new laboratory some sixty miles from New York City. A new Magnifying Transmitter was built and Tesla again claimed to have transmitted power across the globe. The next step in his plan was to build a Magnifying Transmitter at the Niagara Falls power plant and begin the full-time transmission of energy around the world. From this tower, Tesla planned to beam a system of global time, news, stock market reports, music, secret government communication, international banking services, marine navigation, printing data. He even conjured with the possibility of communicating with beings on other planets.

This new project never materialized. The private financing Tesla sought was totally insufficient to match his unpaid bills and, in 1905, his Long Island laboratory was closed down.

Although Tesla continued to think up new inventions, his fires had burned out. From our perspective at the end of the twentieth century, it is a little easier to see why Tesla's genius was eclipsed. In 1900, Max Planck suggested that energy existed in finite units or quanta. In 1905, Einstein published his first paper on Relativity and showed that matter and energy are interconvertible. The first decades of the century were alive with staggering advances in physics. In a revolutionary surge of intellectual power, the foundations laid down by Isaac Newton were totally overturned.

Then, the eyes of the scientific world turned to the Solvay conferences where Einstein, Curie, Planck, Lorentz, Dirac, Pauli, Heisenberg, de Broglie, Born and Bohr sat round a single table and discussed the secrets of nature. Tesla was never a participant in such meetings, in all probability he was never invited for the inventor already belonged to a forgotten age of Newtonian physics.

A careful reading of Tesla's patents and articles shows that, in his later life, he anticipated many of the discoveries of the twentieth century. In 1917, for example, he proposed using short wavelength radio waves to detect ships at sea. Reflections of these high frequency waves by the ships were to be picked up and displayed on cathode ray tubes   a striking anticipation of radar. Yet, in the same year, Einstein wrote his paper on the 'Cosmological Considerations on the General Theory of Relativity'.

The difference between the two incdents is profound: both are, in a sense, speculations yet Einstein's paper was to have the greater scientific impact. The reason is not difficult to understand. Tesla's idea was a combination of insight and deduction, yet it remained only an idea, a brilliant proposal and an educated estimation of possibilities. To be taken further than speculation, Tesla would have had to build a working system, publish details of its construction, give accounts of the various experiments he performed and allow the result to come under scientific scrutiny. Alternatively, he could have published a detailed account of the Theory of Radar, discussing the mechanism of scattering and reflection, presenting calculations of the magnitude of effects and showing exactly how such apparatus could be built.

But, as with so many of Tesla's intuitive predictions, the idea was never taken far enough. Possibly an example may emphasize the point I'm making. Over the past ten years I have investigated the foundations of Quantum Theory and its unification with General Relativity. During that period, I have developed a number of insights, worked at several theoretical approaches and accumulated masses of notes and calculations on various aspects of the problem. It would not be too difficult for me to make a number of intuitive predictions as to how physics will evolve in the twenty-first century. If these speculations turned out to be correct I would not expect to be hailed as the genius who invented or discovered these break-throughs. For the real work lies in starting with an insight and then building it into a full theory. This is what Albert Einstein did in each of his papers on relativity. Beginning with a clearly stated hypothesis and proceeding in logically connected steps he was able to derive mathematical formulae and use them to make concrete predictions. Although Einstein's work on co-smology and relativity is highly imaginative, the mathematics is crystal clear and can be checked by any scientist who reads the paper. In addition, the predictions are unambiguous and can be tested by experiment.

Tesla for his part, and despite his many predictions, was not a scientist in the sense of Einstein, Planck or Heisenberg. He was an inventor and experimenter with a gift of intuition which amounted to genius. But once his financial backers played shy and he could no longer work in his laboratory Tesla was lost. This energetic inventor simply did not possess the tempera-ment and, in all probability, the mathematical background to develop his intuitions on paper. Instead of becoming one of the leading scientists working at the frontiers of science in the early twentieth century, his predictions were confined to sensational newspaper articles only.

As time passed Tesla withdrew even more from human contact. He became eccentric and developed several phobias. In 1937 he was struck by a taxi but refused to seek medical help. From that time until his death he avoided all but his closest friends and confined himself to the Hotel New Yorker and his dialogues to the flock of pigeons he enticed into his room.

Increasingly feeble in mind and body, Nikola Tesla lived on

into his eighties, and he died on January 7, 1943.

Although Einstein's later years were fraught with scientific frustration as he worked in vain at his Unified Field Theory, they were years of health and intellectual activity. At his death, Einstein's fame had reached every country in the world. Nikola Tesla was virtually forgotten.

The boy who vowed to exceed the potential of his dead brother had known fame and then lost it. He was able to force his way onto the pages of America's newspapers but, as he reached middle age, it was not with reports of engineering triumphs but with talk of death rays and a machine which would split the earth apart like an apple. He wrote of war:

> But now, what is the next phase in this evolution? Not peace as yet, by any means. The next change which should naturally follow from modern developments should be the continuous diminution of the number of individuals engaged in battle. The apparatus will be one of specifically great power, but only a few individuals will be required to operate it. This evolution will bring more and more into prominence a machine or mechanism with the fewest individuals as an element of warfare, and the absolutely unavoidable consequence of this will be the abandonment of large, clumsy, slowly moving, and un-manageable units. Greatest possible speed and maximum range of energy-delivery by war apparatus will be the main object. The loss of life will become smaller and smaller, and finally, the number of individuals continuously diminishing, as merely machines will meet in contest without bloodshed, the nations being simply interested, ambitious spectators. When this happy condition is realized, peace will be assured. But, no matter to what degree of perfection rapid-fire guns, high-power cannon, explosive projectiles, torpedo-boats, or other implements of war may be brought, no matter how destructive they may be made, that condition can never be reached through any such development. All such implements require men for their operation; men are indispensable

parts of the machinery. Their object is to kill and destroy. Their power resides in their capacity for doing well. So long as men meet in battle, there will be bloodshed. Bloodshed will ever keep up barbarous passion. To break this fierce spirit, a radical departure must be made, an entirely new principle must be introduced, something that never existed before in warfare – a principle which will forcibly, unavoidably, turn battle into mere spectacle, a play, a contest without loss of blood. To bring this result men must be dispensed with: machine must fight machine. But how to accomplish that which seems impossible? The answer is simple enough: produce a machine capable of acting as though it were part of a human being – no mere mechanical contrivance, comprising levers, screws, wheels, clutches, and nothing more, but a machine embodying a higher principle which will enable it to perform its duties as though it had intelligence, experience, reason, judgement, a mind! This conclusion is the result of my thoughts and observations which have extended through virtually my whole life.

How curious, the tragedy of warfare was to be eliminated by robots. To be truly successful, such a robot would have to experience vicarious suffering on our behalf – a scapegoat of considerable sophistication.

The automatons so far constructed had 'borrowed minds', so to speak, as each merely formed part of the distant operator who conveyed to it his intelligent orders; but this art is only the beginning. I propose to show that, however impossible it may now seem, an automaton may be contrived which will have its 'own mind', and by this I mean that it will be able, independent of any operator, left entirely to itself, to perform, in response to external influences affecting its sensitive organs, a great variety of acts and operations as if it had intelligence. It will be able to follow a course laid out or obey orders given far in advance; it will be capable of distinguishing between what it ought and what it ought not to do, and of making experiences or, otherwise stated, of recording impressions which will definitely affect its subsequent actions. In fact I have already conceived such a plan.

A few years later his philosophy of war was to become even blacker:

> I believed at one time that war could be stopped by making it more destructive, but I found that I was mistaken. We cannot abolish war by outlawing it. We cannot end it by disarming the strong. War can be stopped, not by making the strong weak but by making every nation, weak or strong, able to defend itself, and as you know I was fortunate enough to evolve a new idea and to perfect means which can be used chiefly for defense. If it is adopted, it will revolutionize the relations between nations. It will make any country, large or small, impregnable against armies, air, and other means of attack. My invention requires a large plant, but once it is established it will be possible to destroy anything – men or machines – approaching within a radius of 200 miles. If no country can be attacked successfully, there can be no purpose in war.
>
> My discovery ends the menace of airplanes or submarines, but it insures the supremacy of the battleship, because they can be provided with some of the equipment. I state explicitly that my idea does not contemplate the use of any so-called 'death rays'. I may not live to see my idea accepted, but a century from now every nation will render itself immune from attack by my device. Many thousands of horsepower can be transmitted with my apparatus by a stream thinner than a hair, so that nothing can resist.

This last passage sent a shiver down my spine. Could this brilliant man have been so naïve about the horror of war as to have spoken so glibly about robot killers and an ultimate deathray? There is a blackness behind the hysterical optimism that war will end with the building of his weapons of destruction. Nikola Tesla has become transformed into the stereotype mad scientist of the movies. Professor K. B. Vargan in Leslie Charteris's 1920's thriller *The Last Hero* (later retitled *The Saint Closes the Case*) is the inventor of a 'diabolic' ray which will make war unthinkable. The crazed fictional inventor and his 'ultimate' weapon are not too distant from Nikola Tesla in his later life. If Tesla had been forgotten, I could not help thinking, thank God that these writings about war had been forgotten too.

Chapter Fourteen

SEVERAL WEEKS LATER Andrew Microwski phoned to say that he was giving a party to celebrate C. W. Carter's retirement from the Canadian Senate. He wondered if I would be interested in attending, particularly as an added attraction would be the chance to meet Dr. Puharich.

The reception was held in a roof-top room at Andrew's apartment building. I arrived in the late afternoon to find the room already packed with guests and with few faces that I could recognize. In one corner Senator Carter was talking to a group of friends which included Andrew Microwski, so I went over and introduced myself. After a little conversation I wandered away and joined one of the smaller groups which had formed in the room.

I had assumed that most of the guests would be political friends of the Senator, newspaper people, aides, civil servants and the like, but as I listened to their conversation, I realized that many of the invited guests, while having jobs within the government in Canada and the U.S., had a common interest in esoteric and fringe science. One topic of discussion, for example, was the Spruce Budworm, tiny insect responsible for the destruction of many spruce trees. A new technique for control had been developed by one of the guests which involved taking a photograph of the worm (or was it the tree?) and putting the print inside a black box. I did not attend to the explanation too carefully, but it seemed that by a process of meditation, 'radionic waves' emanated from the box and set to work upon the budworm. Later the conversation turned to that of a man who possessed secret esoteric knowledge which would enable him to integrate modern physics with the occult sciences.

As if to disprove my earlier conjecture on the concentration of practitioners of esoteric arts within the room, I discovered that the group next to me were discussing the merits of seafoods from the Atlantic coast.

The atmosphere of the party was warm and friendly and we chatted on into early evening. Puharich had yet to arrive but I sensed that an entrance was imminent for, amidst the talk of 'natural forces', 'holistic physics' and 'other spaces', eyes would dart towards the door at the other end of the room. I too was eager to meet the mysterious doctor for, from the remarks being passed about him, he appeared to be an exceptional man possessed of powers quite out of the ordinary.

I had met and talked with several 'great men' during my life – Bertrand Russell, Paul Dirac, Werner Heisenberg and even spent several days with a small group including the Indian thinker, J. Krishnamurti, who had, in his youth, been regarded as a god. Yet all these men appeared as people who were no more than human: exceptional in insight and intelligence they may have been but people all the same. I recalled that I had heard Menuhin play the Elgar violin concertos, and on another occasion, Nureyev dance in Swan Lake. Both had appeared to transcend the limitations of their physical form yet I had no doubt that they too were mortal men. So what of Andrija Puharich?

I glanced outside and noticed that the light had begun to fade. Soon after Andrew left the reception. Moments later a murmur ran through the room as heads turned towards the door. Puharich entered in the company of several others and walked briskly across the room. I got up from my chair and went over to what quickly became a throng of interested people. Finding myself on the outside of the group, I turned away and noticed a dark haired woman who was pouring herself a drink. She looked up and smiled at me. I had seen her enter the room with Andrija Puharich.

'Are you a friend of Andrew's?' she asked.

'Yes, we travel together.'

I offered to get her some food but she seemed content with a drink. I poured another for myself and asked her: 'Are you a colleague of Dr. Puharich? I wonder what sort of an interest you've got in this Tesla business?'

She laughed at me. 'No, I help Andrija with his experiments.'

'Really? What exactly do you do? Are you a physicist?'

She smiled at me again, 'I'm his guide. I help him on his journeys.'

I was a little puzzled but did not feel it polite to cross-question her. She turned her drink in her hand for a few moments, then decided to help me out.

'We make journeys to different worlds, different planets. Andrija is interested in all the different intelligences in the universe and I act as his guide. I help him communicate so he can get scientific knowledge from these worlds.'

Several other people had joined us and were listening to her explanation.

'Are these planets in our own space or is it something like different astral planes?' I asked.

'It's hard to say – they are different worlds. Sometimes when I come into a room full of people I see a lot of other people from these worlds.' She began to laugh again, 'You have to be careful not to step on them sometimes'.

I felt a hand on my shoulder and turned to see Andrew Microwski standing beside me.

'David, come and meet Dr. Puharich.'

Andrew led me into the group gathered around Puharich and introduced me. Andrija Puharich bent forward and shook my hand without any recognition in his eyes. I felt slightly embarrassed and explained to him.

'I wrote the N.R.C. report on Tesla power transmission.'

'Oh?'

'I'm afraid that I was a bit hard on your paper. Maybe we could talk about it some time?'

Puharich was silent for a few moments, then nodded his head, 'Yes, why don't we?'

He fell silent again then turned to Andrew, 'Did you manage to get those weather satellite pictures for me?'

'No, I'm afraid not. The Canadian Government doesn't work 24 hours a day.'

Puharich became quite animated again, 'Pity. I would like to have seen what was happening during the black-out.'

'Is this about some new weather modification experiment?' I asked.

Puharich shook his head and began to explain to the group around him: a recent power black-out had clearly been caused by the Russians. He had been standing on his balcony in New York City one night when he saw a glow appear and grow around a power station. The glow continued until the station experienced a blow-out.

'They were ionizing the air around the transformers. I could see it from my balcony,' he said.

There were a host of questions and Puharich began to explain how important it was for the government to realize what was going on. The Russians had new and highly sophisticated weapons based on Tesla's inventions. Not only could they beam energy anywhere in the world and modify the weather, they could also direct a beam to the heart of any city.

'You have got to act right away before it's too late,' he said looking around, 'but, in fact, it's too late already.'

He went even further and explained that the same radiation could be used on civilian populations in a city to control behaviour. The Russians could use 'riot inducing' frequencies to precipitate violence and looting. I turned away, I did not like what was going on and I realized that there was little chance of talking seriously with Puharich that evening.

Later that night I realized how much Puharich's remarks had angered me. It seemed that so much of what I had heard from Tesla's supporters was tinged with fear or paranoia. First, it had been secret Russian experiments to disrupt the weather, rumours of spies and secret agents and now scientists, at work in far-off laboratories, who were supposed to be affecting our brains, inducing riots and blacking-out city power.

I had seen others gripped by occasional paranoia but nothing of this magnitude. Was it really necessary I wondered to invoke secret weapons and the threat of mind-control in order to draw attention to Tesla's name?

On the other hand, if Puharich saw himself in that long tradition of adepts to hidden knowledge then he was certainly behaving true to form. It seems axiomatic that those in pursuit of occult secrets act from time to time in quite arbitrary ways and preach the most disturbing nonsense to their students. George Ivanovitch Gurdjieff's followers flocked to his Institute for the Harmonious Development of Man in France only to be met with hard work, strict discipline, profound psychological insight, layer upon layer of mystification, revilement, requests for money and, in the case of female acolytes, rapid seduction.

By comparison, Puharich's behaviour was quite mild.

I found it difficult to sleep that night and, despite the late hour, got up and wandered round the house in a restless fashion. I walked over to my bookshelves and ran my fingers along the spines. A particular title would evoke a memory and I would pull out the book, read the opening paragraph, then throw it down in disgust or boredom.

In the end I made myself a large glass of whisky, honey and hot water and allowed Scriabin's music to sweep into me. The music from the record player painted its own pictures in my mind and below them I could sense a memory that had been nagging me during the past few days.

The memory had almost the quality of a dream about it.

* * * * *

It was summer and I had been staying for several weeks on an island in Lake Ontario. The cottage I was renting was located a few yards from the lake and each morning I would get up quite early to catch the first fish of the day. A mile or so across the water I could see a tall radio or television tower which had been built on one of the many other small islands which fill that part of the lake.

Over the last few days the weather had been hot and humid. An oppression built in the air until, that evening, it became clear that a storm was brewing. Electrical storms are not infrequent in that location and are caused by cold air from the north meeting warmer air over the lake. On the previous evenings the sky had been alive with electrical discharges although no thunder could be heard.

Just as the light was fading, heavy rain began to fall and almost at once a clap of thunder echoed across the lake. I stayed indoors at first but as the storm grew closer I went to the door and stepped outside to look. The night was a dense black with the only light coming from the windows and open door of the cottage. The rain was heavy and the air seemed alive with thunder and flashes of lightning, the trees around the cottage were bent by the force of the wind.

The centre of the storm came closer and I suddenly realized that the last stream of lightning had hit the water somewhere between the cottage and the transmitting tower whose red lights I could just make out through the rain. A blast of thunder hit simultaneously with the blinding effect of the lightning. I tensed myself in anticipation of another flash when I realized that something peculiar was happening. Around me the wind and rain had ceased and I felt terribly isolated. I looked at a nearby tree and realized that it was no longer bent by the wind but upright and quivering with each leaf set in violent motion to and fro. At the same time I realized that something was wrong with the scene in front of me for the whole area seemed to be filled with black patches – holes in the world almost. I could swear that these black areas were not created by my own eyes, but were actually located 'out there'. At the same time, I became aware of a strange hissing sound – like the sound of a rope being lashed through the air. Then, suddenly, an almighty explosion enveloped me and it was all over, rain and wind returned and the storm continued as before.

In that frozen instant I had seen no flash, no streak of lightning. I had simply experienced the sound, the pressure of an explosion which seemed to come from no direction but was all around me. I went back inside the cottage and attempted in vain to sort out what had happened.

The next morning I looked outside and could only find a few broken branches and twigs which had been ripped from the trees by the force of the storm. Around the cottage there had been no other damage. There was one curious after-effect, however, which I shall record here but which I hesitate to associate with my mysterious experience. That same morning I discovered that the battery in my car was totally dead. The car had been driven regularly and had worked perfectly the day before. The ignition was still switched off and no lights or other electrical apparatus had been left on by mistake, but the battery had totally discharged. I had owned the car for a couple of years and it remained with me for two or three years more. In all that time I experienced nothing similar with this same battery.

In the depths of winter I had almost drained it with a few false starts of the engine and while there would not be sufficient current to turn the starter, the clock and radio, would still run and the lights glow faintly.

But that morning the battery was totally dead and the clock stopped at around eleven o'clock. Since I had used the car on the previous day, the clock must have stopped the previous night – around the time of the storm. Very strange!

* * * * *

The next morning I realized the connection between Puharich's remarks at the party and what had happened during that storm. While I was still not willing to believe a story of mind-bending rays put to political use, I began to wonder if electrical disturbances could have an effect on the human brain? Had something of that nature happened to me during the storm I had watched over Lake Ontario?

I continued to take an interest in Tesla's ideas over the next few months and in particular the possibility of the biological effects of storms and electrical disturbances. I was, therefore, very interested to learn that a laboratory was being constructed in Ottawa to study the biological effects of 'Non-Ionizing Radiation'.

Chapter Fifteen

NON-IONIZING RADIATION: it is one of those curious idiosyncrasies of nature that once you hear of a new writer or filmstar or even learn the meaning of an obscure word, it keeps cropping up again and again. Common sense tells us that it has always been around in books, newspapers and conversation, but after we are sensitized to a word or name we begin to see it all around us.

Common sense may be right but in the privacy of our secret selves we may sometimes wonder if such coincidences have something magical about them. Carl Jung thought that there was and called these 'meaningful co-incidences' Synchronicity.

In my case coincidence, or was it Synchronicity, began when I first began to think about the biological effects of low frequency (or 'Non-ionizing') radiation. To my surprise, I learned that a laboratory was being built in the area to study the biological effects of radio and microwaves. Within a few weeks several articles on very low frequency radiation turned up on my desk and my friend, David Schrum in Sudbury, spoke to a scientist who was working in the same field.

Things seemed to have advanced a great deal from that day, back in 1899, when Nikola Tesla discovered that the earth was alive with electrical power. Today a variety of natural electrical signals had been measured and characterized. In short, the first charts of that great electrical ocean first discovered by Nikola Tesla had been drawn up.

Electrical fields arise from several different sources on earth. First there is the large voltage difference between the earth's surface and the upper atmosphere. Then there is the fluctuating difference in voltage between thunder clouds and the earth. In addition to these differences of electrical potential, there are waves of electromagnetic energy which are produced by weather fronts, thunderstorms and other atmospheric changes. Finally, there are electrical effects arising from shock waves in the earth's crust. Earthquakes, volcanoes and the daily move- ment of fault lines produce mechanical pressure waves which travel around the earth. As they pass through certain rock formations, electromagnetic fields are created which then travel across the earth.

So Tesla was perfectly correct, the earth *is* alive with the electrical movement of storms, weather changes and the movement of its rocky crust. It so happens that most of these signals are of extremely low frequency and are, therefore, called by the name 'ELFs'. Any one who has heard a marching band in the far distance will realize that the bass notes carry farthest. The same thing applies to electromagnetic radiation and waves of extremely low frequency can travel right around the earth.

The ELFs from weather fronts vibrate at around 100 cycles per second to one cycle every ten seconds, far lower than the millions of cycles per second used in short wave radio broadcasts. The interference signals from Riga were in the high frequency spectrum but occurred in pulses or bursts of about nine per second.

The lower the frequency of a radio wave the longer is its wavelength. When it comes to waves which oscillate at just a few cycles per second, the wavelengths are about the same size as the earth itself. A wave which fits exactly around the earth sets up a powerful resonance. Tesla proposed to pump energy from his Magnifying Transmitter at just this frequency, called the Schumann resonance.

What do ELFs and Schumann resonances have to do with the human brain and mood-changing beams? There is no simple answer but I think that I can attempt a little speculation. Life evolved on earth in the midst of this electrical ebb and flow. It began with complex molecules, then single-celled organisms and finally the profusion of animal and plant life that covers the planet today.

Life is a self-regulating electro-chemical process which is both sensitive to its outer environment and at the same time able to stabilize internal fluctuations. It is not improbable that living things developed a special sensitivity to external electrical fields wherever there was an advantage to be gained.

The simple organisms respond to external fields in the laboratory and higher animals, such as birds, fish and seals, can orient themselves by using the earth's magnetic pole. When it comes to humans, there is considerable evidence that we are sensitive to changes in electrical and maganetic fields and certain individuals have developed the power to detect minute fluctuations. Some dowsers who have been tested in the laboratory are able to detect electrical currents as these are passed through concealed wires.

There is other circumstantial evidence which suggests that the complex electrical circuits of the human brain are influenced by radiation at various frequencies. In the U.S.S.R. safety standards for non-ionizing radiation are far more stringent than in the West and their laboratories have reported such effects as nausea, headaches, 'buzzings' in the ears and mood changes in connection with low frequency radiation. It is only within the last few years that any attempt has been made to study these effects in Western laboratories.

The Schumann resonance itself – that frequency at which the whole planet resonates with electrical energy – occurs in the same frequency range as human brain waves. ELFs which are produced in high pressure areas on clear days have similar frequency to human rhythms. The so-called α-state is associated with a calm and alert brain. Delta rhythms associated with deep sleep fall into exactly the same frequency range as ELFs produced on cloudy, low pressure days. The hypothesis that our brains are in a state of electrical sympathy with the electrical ocean outside, although not proven, is distinctly persuasive.

Tesla's Magnifying transmitter, which some people claimed had been built in Riga, was supposed to operate in a similar frequency range. Could such a transmitter affect the human brain? Some scientists believed that radiation produced before earthquakes could induce mood changes for people in the surrounding countryside. I had read stories of animals and birds which desert an area hours or even days before an earthquake and of people who experienced nightmares of premonition. Now there seemed to be an edge of truth to these anecdotes. Stresses which are released shortly before the main quake would set up shock waves in the surrounding rock. Under compression certain rock formations produce electrical fields which would then travel as ELFs away from the potential quake centre.

The possibility that animals and humans living in an earthquake zone could experience feelings of dread and unease in the hours before a major shock no longer seemed an old wives' tale. ELFs could very well induce changes in the brain which would then be experienced as warnings. If ELFs from earthquakes, then why not the radiation from a Tesla Transmitter; after all the Tesla device worked in exactly the same frequency range close to the Schumann resonance. But if I was about to accept the effects of Tesla transmissions on consciousness, then what about the Riga experiments?

Although I hated to admit the possibility, I was forced to argue that the pulses or bursts of interference occurred at between 6 and 20 times per second, right within the ELF range. Could Puharich actually have been right? Had Andrew Microwski's warning of mood-modifying beams some basis in fact? I hoped with all my heart that it was just another fairy story.

Chapter Sixteen

THE TALK OF Tesla Transmitters faded from the newspapers. P.A.C.E., however, was still active. On one occasion
I was invited to a meeting at which a latter-day Tesla revealed
an amazing invention which could be built with 'materials
purchased at any hardware store'. It was supposed to tap into a
source of 'cosmic energy' and, like Tesla's invention, it could
transmit this power without wires.

The inventor's claims were astounding; he could transmit a
narrow beam of power of such intensity that it would burn a
hole right through the moon. His device was certainly versatile
for it could also be used to cure cancer. I remained to be
convinced and even though the instrument was the sort of thing
that could be built for a few dollars worth of pipe and wire, I
was never to see it in operation. After an initial meeting, a
demonstration was set up for which I obtained a movie camera
and film. Only hours before the appointed time, my phone rang
and I was told that the instrument had 'burned out' - no doubt
it had overloaded itself with a liberal dose of 'cosmic energy'!

Andrew Microwski's energies and enthusiasm continued
unabated, for P.A.C.E. was now producing an interesting
newsletter containing articles on Nikola Tesla and reviews
from the frontiers of science. From time to time, I would
phone him for a chat. On the last occasion I spoke to him, he
told me that the signals from Riga had stepped up in intensity
during the U. S. Presidential campaign, then stopped altogether the day before Ronald Reagan was elected President.
That certainly begs comment.

Of Andrija Puharich I saw no more. Some time after my
report for the National Research Council, he had gone into

hiding. His house and laboratory had burned to the ground and Puharich could not be found. Later Andrew Microwski received a call from Puharich with the request to make no attempt to contact or trace him.

There was a rumour that Puharich had been forced to flee for his life from the attentions of foreign intelligence agencies. The whole story seemed to be tied up with mindbending radiations and Tesla Transmitting Towers. Later I heard that Puharich was working in Mexico with a psychic healer.

In the past Andrew Microwski had hinted that spies from several countries were interested in Tesla's work. Arthur Matthews, Tesla's surviving assistant, said that 'men with Russian sounding names' had been to see him and even Tim Richardson, whom I considered fairly level headed, had told me of people nosing around outside his laboratory.

Were foreign spies really trying to obtain Tesla's secrets? Had they actually gone as far as to threaten Puharich's life? I tend to be particularly cynical when it comes to intelligence agencies. To begin with, the whole business often seems very childish and hardly likely to promote world peace and trust amongst nations. But then I suppose I'm in danger of sounding like Baron Raglan who, in the Crimean War, refused to listen to an agent's intelligence on the enemy's movement because it wasn't the gentlemanly thing to do.

I have, however, lived through the late sixties where everyone fancied that they were under surveillance because their telephone made a mysterious series of clicks each time they picked it up. If an unmarked car was parked across from one's apartment, or a letter was mysteriously delayed, then clearly 'they' were stepping up their campaign of surveillance. For my part, I began to wonder where this giant army of spies was housed and fed since, to keep so many people under close observation, would take tens of thousands of agents.

When it came to Nikoa Tesla, I was at first inclined to take these stories of spies with a generous pinch of salt. After all what could they possibly learn that was not already contained in a host of patents and articles? As usual the allegations were vague, yet on one occasion a name cropped up and when I checked back I discovered that the same name had been mentioned before. With some difficulty and a measure of innocent deception, I managed to trace the name to an intelligence agency and eventually talked to the man in question.

His answers were vague and non-committal but they did bear out Andrew Microwski's spy story.

I was never really able to uncover the whole story of the intelligence operations which surrounded the work of Nikola Tesla and his latter-day followers but I did obtain a few hints. To begin with, after talking with the intelligence agent who had been involved with P.A.C.E., I had the feeling that the organization in itself was not the object of interest. P.A.C.E. and the Tesla Transmitter seemed more like a tasty piece of cheese and the intelligence agency took the form of a cat. The cat was not particularly interested in cheese but in the rats who crawled out of the woodwork to nibble. By keeping a low profile and hanging around the cheese, I had the feeling that a certain intelligence agency hoped to have a close look at a particular group of rats.

A curious coincidence provided another piece of the puzzle. One afternoon I was sitting in my favourite restaurant talking to a friend of mine. The atmosphere was relaxed and my friend was talking about 'unexplained phenomena', and the various occult experiences she had come across in her life. Suddenly she stood up and waved at someone who had just entered the café. My friend whispered to me that the new arrival possessed unusual powers, then called out to her to come over to our table.

The afternoon was warm and I had washed down a plate of hummus with several glasses of wine. Rather than join in the conversation, I listened, half asleep, to the talk about reincarnation, astral voyages and hidden knowledge.

My friend mentioned how many important people had become involved in the paranormal, some of them quite high in the government. The visitor agreed and mentioned a group which fostered the development of psychic powers. I listened with half an ear until she mentioned the name of the man who was assisting her. She mentioned that he possessed considerable ability and was able to hypnotize people and lead them through past lives.

The name she mentioned caused my mind to jump into gear. What on earth was an intelligence agent doing in the middle of a group of psychics. What did the paranormal powers of the mind have to do with Tesla transmission?

I had been able to trace a connection between mood modification and ELFs. Presumably, since the Tesla Frequencies fell in the same range they would have an effect on human beings. But did all this have a connection with international spying?

Although the cold war belonged to an earlier time, the seventies was a decade of new weapons, weapons which could think. All the research which had been directed towards machine intelligence and computers which could see and recognize objects had a military spin-off. Post war research had initially been directed towards bigger and better rockets, delivery systems which could carry more destructive power over greater distances.

The new generation of weapons are able to think and see, they are capable of avoiding radar early warning systems by travelling at high speeds close to the ground and their electronic intelligence enables them to recognize terrain, avoid obstacles and direct themselves towards a target.

Wars of the future will also take place in space. Already a number of military satellites have been placed in orbit and a new generation of space craft makes it possible to pluck a satellite from space and return it to earth. Along with the intelligent missile and space warfare comes the gas dynamic laser and the particle beam weapon.

With an output of several million watts, a military laser can cut through the metal shielding of a missile in flight. Since the beam of energy moves at the speed of light there is little room for any manoeuvre of avoidance. The beam can be aimed almost directly at a military satellite or high speed missile to shoot down or ignite its payload.

Even more dramatic in its effect is the hypothetical particle beam weapon. Research in modern particle physics has led to the building of elementary particle accelerators of higher and higher energy. Not only can elementary particles such as high energy electrons, protons and neutrons be produced by such machines but heavier nuclei and ions can be whipped up to speeds approaching that of light. The kinetic energy contained in such a beam is enormous. The beam itself can be focussed into a narrow path and directed almost at the speed of light towards a missile.

Beside such weapons, what significance could a late nineteenth century invention hold and what use would 'paranormal' powers be to national security? I found the answer one day when I was discussing safe levels of radiation with another scientist. It turned out that my scientific colleague had once been involved in weapons research.

'What's the worst thing you can do to the enemy?' he asked me.

I shrugged, 'Well, kill them I suppose. Blow them up?'

He shook his head and smiled at my simplistic answer.

'People can be replaced. In modern warfare you can replace people in the front line fairly quickly. But if you injure them, that could be far worse.'

He explained that an injury requires a decision, it may tie up several people to give treatment and fly out the wounded soldier. Even worse is an officer who is disabled but remains in command.

A weapon which would produce nausea, confusion, forgetfulness and irritability could devastate an opponent. After all, history shows us that wavering ambiguous orders and blundering decisions can more effectively turn a battle than fire power alone. A badly worded order caused Lord Cardigan to lead the Light Brigade to charge down the 'Valley of Death' into heavy Russian armaments instead of securing the lightly defended Vorontsov Heights.

In the campaigns which led up to the Battle of Waterloo, Napoleon's various physical disabilities seem to have taken a heavy toll upon his military genius. Errors of judgement during the battle, as much as Wellington's nerve and Blucher's determination to arrive on time, seem to have contributed to the French defeat.

A battle can be won or lost on an army's morale and the character of its commander. Clearly a device which could subtly undermine the will to fight and the ability to make clear and immediate decisions would be of considerable interest to military intelligence all over the world.

But did such a weapon exist? Could a Tesla Transmitter be tuned to emit disabling radiation towards an opposing army? Could it be so arranged as to disrupt the normal life of a civilian population by promoting irritability, minor illnesses, loss of concentration and the like?

If this were true then Tesla's invention had certainly been used for evil ends. What had once started out as a plan to free the human race would have ended up as yet another form of enslavement. Was there no ray of hope in all this?

Chapter Seventeen

ONE AFTERNOON, FEELING at a low ebb, I was browsing in my local library. In the middle of one of the shelves, I noticed the title *Uri Geller*. That sounded interesting. I had met Geller and had once been interested in his paranormal abilities. I took the book from the shelf and saw that it had been written by the English author, Colin Wilson. Several years ago Wilson and I had exchanged letters. I knew that he was interested in the future development of human abilities and the evolution of the conscious mind. As I stood in the library and thumbed through the book, the thought struck me that Nikola Tesla, with his dreams of the future and his unusual ability to create inventions in his imagination, would be the sort of person to appeal to Colin Wilson's interest.

I walked home with the book and was soon immersed in the text. I read the book in one sitting and learned of Wilson's meeting with Geller and saw the name Andrija Puharich crop up again and again. Suddenly it struck me that I should write a book on my encounter with Tesla. A lack of focus I had felt during the past weeks must have been some subtle message from my unconscious mind telling me that I should not leave Tesla behind. Even if I had no faith in Tesla Power Transmission I could not bring myself to leave his work in some dry government report.

I began at once to plan out how I would write the book, telling myself that I would have to spend several weeks in the National Archives and the Science Library looking up references. But as I began to collect all my material together a curious thought struck me. I realized that in one sense I had no need of all this material, for the book was already mapped out somewhere in my head and was simply waiting to be written. I felt that it was rather like one of Tesla's inventions which sprang ready made into his imagination.

The book I would write would be far from an academic study of Power Transmission or a careful history of Tesla's life. Instead it would carry the flavour of my interaction with a man long dead. It would tell how I came to see the shadows and echoes of Tesla's dreams and how two scientists from different times and different cultures were, in some curious way, able to reach across the gulf which separated them.

What I had captured from Tesla's life was a series of vivid impressions, points of contact across a century of time. Out of all of these, I was struck most vividly by the inventor's account of what had happened that afternoon in Budapest when, during a walk, the invention of the induction motor had appeared to him.

Tesla's life was steeped in enigma yet his greatest mystery was crystal clear. The plans of his inventions had appeared *crystal clear* in a waking vision. Was Tesla blessed with some unique gift of hidden knowledge or had this experience occurred to other men of genius, and to a lesser extent, to the whole of humankind?

It did not take me long to find a number of examples from the lives of other scientists, artists and inventors. Two will suffice.

> I turned my chair to the fire and dozed. Again the atoms were gambolling before my eyes. This time the smaller groups kept modestly in the background. My mental eye, rendered more acute by repeated visions of this kind, could now distinguish larger structures, of manifold conformation; long rows, sometimes more closely fitted together; all twining and twisting in snakelike motion. But look! What was that? One of the snakes had seized hold of its own tail, and the form whirled mockingly before my eyes. As if by a flash of lightning I awoke.

In consequence of a slight indisposition, an anodyne had

been prescribed, from the effects of which he fell asleep in his chair at the moment he was reading the following sentence, or words of the same substance, in Purchas's Pilgrimage:

> 'Here the Khan Kubla commanded a palace to be built, and a stately garden thereunto. And thus ten miles of fertile ground were enclosed with a wall.'

The Author continued for about three hours in a profound sleep, at least of the external senses, during which time he has the most vivid confidence, that he could not have composed less than from two to three hundred lines; if that indeed can be called composition in which all the images rose up before him as *things* with a parallel production of the correspondent expressions, without any sensation of consciousness of effort.

The first is an account of how the German chemist, von Kekulé, discovered the structure of the benzene molecule in 1865 and the second, related in the third person, describes Coleridge's composition of the poem *Kubla Kahn*.

These two passages are strikingly similar to Tesla's own account. In all cases it appears that a period of concentration on some problem has been followed by relaxation. During the latter receptive period a graphic vision appears which is complete and entire.

Nikola Tesla had trained his memory and was, therefore, able to retain the vision in all its detail when he came to build his working models and write down detailed plan drawings. Coleridge was not so lucky, for while copying down his vision he was interrupted by a visitor from the village of Porlock and the complete poem was lost to the world.

Any creative worker knows that, after a long period spent worrying about an 'insoluble' problem, the answer will come during a period of relaxation or recreation when the mind is particularly receptive. At such moments it appears that the mind no longer operates upon 'logical' lines, oscillating this way and that in the face of a paradox of reason. Rather, it leaps across the problem, transcending limitations and producing something creative and new.

Nikola Tesla's ability to create directly from the imagination seems to have been particularly highly developed. Just because other artists have possessed a similar ability does not make it commonplace. Is there perhaps some clue which can guide us into this unknown territory of creativity, this mapless land of the unknown?

Let me leave Nikola Tesla for several pages and attempt to gain some understanding of the ability he possessed in abundance – the power to understand the physical world in some direct, non-rational way. I will begin with another scientist, Wolfgang Pauli.

Some years ago I conducted a series of interviews for radio with several of the founders of Modern Physics. Although Pauli had died several years earlier, his name kept cropping up as the Joker in the scientific pack. Pauli, a genius in his own right, was also the supreme critic, the voice of reason, the measure of other men's theories. He was seen by many older physicists as a scientist of unfailing intuition and one badly needed in our own time to clarify so much of the loose thinking and half-baked ideas which abound.

Pauli had another side, which became of increasing importance to him. He was interested in areas of the mind which would be called mystical by most thinkers. With Carl Jung, he joined in an investigation of what they termed 'Synchronicity'. Pauli had begun by trying to understand how Joannes Kepler had first formulated his laws of planetary motion. He showed that the astronomer had made use of occult images or archetypes as the basis for his thinking.

Later the scientist and the psychologist went further into this world of mind by attempting to chart the parallel flows of matter and thought which take place in our universe.

Carl Jung defined Synchronicity as a meaningful coincidence between physical and mental states. The other term he used for it was an 'Acausal Connecting Principle' between mind and matter, for it dealt with events for which no physical or logical cause and effect relationship was possible.

One could extend Jung's definition to say that Synchronicities were the manifestations of that harmony which exists between the unfolding of the physical and mental universe.

An example from Jung's own life should help. In 1909, he visited Sigmund Freud in Vienna and the conversation turned to parapsychology which held an attraction for Jung and a distaste for Freud. In the heat of the conversation a sudden detonation occurred in Freud's bookcase. The two men started up in surprise and Jung drew attention to the incident as support for his argument. Freud dismissed this as 'sheer bosh' but Jung experienced an inner certainty that the event would occur again. 'I now predict that in a moment there will be another loud report', he said to Freud and sure enough, the even occurred again.

Sigmund Freud was shaken at the time, but soon gained his composure and, in a letter to Jung, joked about his credulity. He also warned Jung against the 'black tide of mud' of occultism.

In the above incident, a psychic crisis was paralleled by two loud reports in Freud's room. It is clearly a case of Synchronicity. For a moment the flow of thought and the events of the physical world exhibited a similar face, the two worlds coalesced and a physical event was flooded with deep meaning.

The rational mind may well feel itself to be in rebellion with such far fetched ideas as Synchronicity and find itself agreeing with Freud that the whole thing is coincidence. Yet the concept of a parallel nature between mind and matter is not new; indeed it is found in Alchemy, the Kabbala and in Classical Indian and Chinese philosophy.

In essence, all these cosmologies speak of a parallelism between the world of physical events and some 'higher' plane. This higher world contains its patterns in some simultaneous or rather timeless sense as equally present. In the world of matter, however, patterns are revealed sequentially as they unroll in time.

The higher plane, therefore, contains all past, present and future situations of our universe but in some simultaneous presence. It is the belief of these philosophies that, through some symbolic ritual or action, it is possible to mirror the eternal patterns in our own world, and by implication, gain a deeper understanding of the meaning of our lives, past, present and future. For example, divination is not a method of 'predicting' the future or even influencing it. Rather, it presents in microcosm a pattern which surrounds our present consciousness and carries with it intimations of past and future.

Casting a hexagram for the I. Ching in no way influences our future or establishes a causal connection which must be followed. No deterministic path is laid down for us to travel once the oracle has been consulted. Rather a Synchronicity is presented between our own world and this supposed higher plane. The information moreover is not presented in any explicit form, as in a Horoscope for example, but is symbolic and enfolded as a pattern of numbers, an arrangement of symbolic forms or in some other fashion which requires deciphering.

If all this talk of Synchronicity, Higher Planes and the I. Ching seems unnecessarily mystical and unfocussed for an understanding of Tesla's visions, I apologise, but it is a symptom of the terrible difficulties one faces when known and familiar territory is abandoned. The ideas I have introduced are no more than hints or clues, they are props which may be abandoned as we proceed on our journey. At most, they can direct our thinking while we walk into this uncharted land. After that we can do with them as we think fit.

This parallelism between mind and matter, this synchronicity of events, is never explicit but generally present in an enfolded or symbolic form. To take the next step in the journey, let us turn to the world of theoretical physics.

Ten years ago I was deeply involved in work on the foundations of Quantum Theory and General Relativity and I began to investigate the way physical laws are written down. The answer was well known: that there is no 'unique' expression of a law of nature, rather an endless number of alternative mathematical expressions, all equally valid. The whole thing is rather like a kaleidoscope in which, as each pattern dissolves, a new one forms and grows. In a similar way the laws of nature and their expression through mathematical descriptions can be transformed according to various mathematical manipulations.

In a fugue a musical shape is transformed through modulation, inversion, reflection, changes in rhythm and instrumentation. The continued movement of the musical shape, according to the laws of fugue, gives life to the entire music. At times, the theme is immediately recognizable, at others it seems hidden and transformed.

In a similar way, the mathematical descriptions of nature can proceed through a series of transformations according to a certain law (The Canonical Transformations). At times, the descriptions are explicit and clear, for they deal in particles, paths and collisions. Yet under a transformation we may be taken into a more subtle world of phase waves and hypersurfaces. Like the kaleidoscope, image upon image is presented to us, some of which are immediately recognizable, others of which are mathematically subtle, yet they are all valid descriptions of nature.

The explicit and obvious descriptions - two billiard balls in collision, a swinging pendulum - are easy to deal with. The subtle descriptions are harder for they require mathemathical untangling before we can interpret them in terms of everyday objects.

David Schrum and I discussed such ideas for many long hours in our office in Ottawa. We began to wonder if these more subtle descriptions may be the natural way of dealing with the quantum world. We guessed, from the perspective of the atom, that particles which move along well defined paths may look just as tangled and incomprehensible as the intersection of abstract hypersurfaces does to inhabitants of the large scale world.

With such thoughs in mind, I made my trip to England only to discover that David Bohm, at the University of London, had pushed the ideas even further with his notion of the Implicate Order. Bohm claimed that a subtle, enfolded pattern stretched across the universe, which he called the Implicate Order. What to us appears clear and explicit is but one aspect of this greater order. Bohm would speak of this as the Explicate Order which had been unfolded from a more general play of forms.

This enfolding and unfolding of order was not some arcane proposition or Kabbalistic hypothesis, for its foundations lay within the framework of Theoretical Physics. The implications were far reaching, for one could speculate that this movement between the explicit and the implicit occurred in thought as well. What would be called the unconscious was in essence the enfolded or implicit movement of the human mind. The analogies with Jung's Synchronicity and the ancient's 'Higher World' order became obvious. A general and subtle movement is common to both matter and mind: when unfolded in a linear sequence it is seen as the movement of thought in time or the motion of material bodies. The appearance of Synchronicity is the manifestation of one of these points of parallelism between the unfolding of matter and of mind. It becomes clear that there is no causal relationship between the two events, no chain of action and reaction which links cause to effect. Both events are simply manifestations which have surfaced from a common ground and represent a chink in our temporal world through which may be glimpsed an intimation of something far deeper.

The circle is completed; from that curious phenomenon of inspiration and insight we have moved into conjectures of parallelism between matter and mind, and from that vantage point hinted at some deeper ground from which matter and mind are born. From this lofty pinnacle, Tesla's gifts of insight and vision seem to dim when placed beside the potential of the whole human race.

To return to the specific, however, it now seems possible to gain some insight into how Nikola Tesla received his visions of mechanical devices. As a young man, he was given to pondering the movements of nature in wind and waterfall. He also experimented with simple mechanical devices and, as a boy, produced his first crude inventions. Then followed a period of intellectual activity at Polytechnic and University where Tesla set himself the problem of an improved electrical motor which could operate without direct current connections. He had already learned the language of mechanics and electricity, he had taken the necessary intellectual steps to define the problem. By the time he left university, Tesla had set forth specific scientific boundaries around the problem as his unconscious mind learned to paint nature's patterns. All that remained was for Tesla to allow the ideas to move along some implicit level until that moment, during his walk, when the idea unfolded before him.

The vision was complete and dramatic: in some sense it had always been with him, but it required that final moment of acceptance and sensitivity before it could burst into his conscious mind like a fully formed flower.

Postscript

SO HERE THE story ends. Or does it?

As I was looking over this manuscript before taking it to my typist, a pamphlet with the title 'My Life Depends on You!' came through my mail box. I flipped it open and began to read the opening sentence:

> I know what I am about to tell you will sound bizarre, almost beyond belief – R.C.M.P. [Royal Canadian Mounted Police] surreptitious testing of a telepathic amplifier that works with microwaves to control people's minds and bodies, voices in the air, spy schools, interrogation, toxic gases – I know how crazy it all sound.'

I smiled as I read on ... after all isn't this where we came in?

The writer of the pamphlet, Martti Koski, claimed that he had been controlled for several months by microwave broadcasts. The details of his experiences were certainly bizarre, invisible voices speaking in Finnish, forbidden foods, mysterious faces, sadistic sexual experiments and elaborate indoctrination involving five fire trucks. I had no knowledge of the writer but his report of 'voices' which controlled his behaviour and forced him to perform such acts as minor thefts and masturbation were not unlike the experiences of the mentally disturbed.

'Microwave Man', as he claimed he had been called, argued that security forces had learned the technique of controlling thought by means of microwaves. In the future, governments, he said, would be able to control dissenters and other troublemakers. He agreed that his story appeared unbelievable, but cautioned that 'if there is, in your mind, the slightest chance what I have to tell holds some truth, doesn't it demand and deserve your further concern?', for

> ... consider the possibilities if microwave manipulation does work. If someone, with control over the technology, could disrupt or direct the workings of people's brains or even wipe some brains clear and insert other data.

But, as I said, the story's over. And as for secret government agencies controlling people's minds with microwaves? Well, I'm inclined to take the whole thing with a very strong pinch of salt.

But you never know. Do you?